An Advanced
Organic
Laboratory
Course

A SERIES OF BOOKS IN CHEMISTRY:
Andrew Streitwieser, Jr., Editor

An Advanced Organic Laboratory Course

MELVIN S. NEWMAN
Regents Professor of Chemistry
OHIO STATE UNIVERSITY

THE MACMILLAN COMPANY, NEW YORK
Collier-Macmillan Limited, London

The Macmillan Company
866 Third Avenue, New York, New York 10022

Collier-Macmillan Canada, Ltd., Toronto, Ontario

Library of Congress catalog card number: 70-155927

First Printing

This book is dedicated to

Rudolph J. Anderson, my Ph.D. preceptor at Yale, who taught me the importance of quality in laboratory work;

Louis F. Fieser, postdoctoral research director at Harvard, who taught me the importance of quantity as well as quality and who showed me how much fun laboratory work can be;

E. B. "Eebie" Hershberg, my laboratory partner at Harvard, who taught me to seek apparatus properly designed for the purpose at hand;

Louis P. Hammett, whose book stimulated me to apply the principles of physical-organic chemistry to the improvement of laboratory work;

Teachers of organic chemistry who believe, as I do, that the improvement of experimental skills is important to the development of research workers;

Bea, my wife, who can always control my reactions.

Preface

For many years I have been giving organic laboratory courses to chemistry majors and graduate students. My hope has been to encourage students to become *superior* laboratory workers. To achieve this primary objective I have tried to introduce students to the concept that they should decide what is to be done and how to do it. At the start a student has little background on which to base decisions. However, during the course given at Ohio State University many lectures are given to provide this background, including detailed discussions of reaction types and the mechanisms involved, descriptions of varied laboratory techniques, and demonstrations of certain techniques. Several of these lectures are given by other faculty members not only because a wider variety of expertise is desirable but also because such lectures provide a fine opportunity for contact between students and faculty. In this book the discussion of the chemistry involved in the various experiments has been kept to a minimum. However, anyone in charge of such a course has the option of emphasizing whatever aspects of the subject seem desirable.

After reading the literature, listening to detailed discussions of laboratory techniques and reaction types and mechanisms, and seeing demonstrations of certain techniques, the student should be able to evaluate critically directions for carrying out any reaction and working up the products.

In order that a student run an "experiment" and not merely follow directions blindly, I judge the success of an experiment *by the material balance and not by the yield of one product*. If yield is the only measure of success, the student will rarely vary reaction conditions or isolation techniques to determine whether the yield or purity of the desired product can be improved. However, if a high material balance is emphasized, two or more students will often agree to test the effect of a variable by comparing results. Thus, the research angle may be introduced into the laboratory course. I cannot stress this aspect too much. After all, teachers of potential M.S. and Ph.D. students should encourage the spirit of research as much as possible. Often, more is learned from a "mistake" than from the successful repetition of a literature preparation.

Another feature of laboratory courses is to encourage students to repeat experiments. Repetition can illustrate how reproducible their own results are and also how much easier it is to run a reaction the second time. Students should understand that no chemical experiment should be reported in the literature unless it has been repeated at least once.

I have often been asked how a student with almost no experience could make a valid suggestion for improving a literature preparation. To this I reply that the question is beside the point. The important thing is that students realize everything written in the literature is not necessarily the gospel. The sooner the student realizes that improvements are possible, the sooner he assumes a research attitude toward laboratory work.

In presenting certain techniques and making recommendations for the use of certain equipment, I do not mean to imply that my advice should be followed blindly. Cost factors in course work must be considered. Also, there is much difference in opinion among chemists. I suggest the reasons for any recommendations to students should be clearly stated. Coverage of apparatus and techniques in this book is obviously incomplete. The experiments chosen are merely representative of the philosophy of this type of laboratory course.

No treatment of infrared, ultraviolet, or nuclear magnetic resonance spectra as an aid to laboratory work is given, nor is there any discussion of vapor-phase chromatography. Many treatments of these approaches are available. Teachers of laboratory courses should use all available instruments, should include lectures about their care and use, and should recommend purchase of suitable specialized books.

I take pleasure in acknowledging the help of Professor John Swenton for contributing Chapter 9 on organic photochemistry and Professor Paul Gassman for contributing Chapter 11 on electrolytic reactions.

I also would like to thank Professors Robert E. Ireland of the California Institute of Technology, Douglas C. Neckers of Hope College, Andrew Streitwieser, Jr., of the University of California at Berkeley, and Daniel Swern of Temple University for valuable criticism of the manuscript.

M. S. N.

Brief Contents

Detailed Contents

Seven

Synthesis of 1-Heptyne 145

Eight

Superheated Steam Distillation 155

Nine

Photolysis of 4,4-Diphenyl-2-cyclohexenone 163

Ten

Ozonization of [—]-β-Pinene to [+]-Nopinone 187

Eleven

Preparation of Bromobenzene from p-Bromoiodobenzene 191

Twelve

Report Writing 203

Appendixes

Index 225

An Advanced Organic Laboratory Course

Introduction

The laboratory work described in this book is intended to encourage the student to approach an experiment with sufficient self-confidence to realize that improvements are always possible, as well as to acquaint the student with a variety of experimental techniques.

Self-confidence with regard to laboratory manipulations can be gained by showing that, with proper attention to detail in procedures for isolating and purifying solid and liquid reaction products, experiments can be carried out routinely with recovery of over 90 % of the products. Specific directions for running reactions are almost never provided. Rather, lectures cover the general principles of the reactions to be carried out. After hearing the lectures and consulting appropriate literature, the student must decide for himself whether to follow exactly or to modify any directions he finds. Before running an experiment, students are advised to consult their instructor or an assistant in the course. From the start, however, students must realize the literature is not holy and that they are entirely capable of making changes that can lead to improvements. An improvement need not necessarily be an improvement in yield. A saving of labor in the isolation and/or purification of the product is an improvement. Many experiments described in the literature have not been submitted to exhaustive study to determine optimum conditions and yields. Furthermore, new reagents and techniques may have been discovered since the work in question was reported.

Experiments involving the use of liquid ammonia, liquid hydrogen fluoride, ozone, vapor-phase reactions, vacuum fractional distillation, electrolytic oxidation or reduction, photochemical transformations, and superheated steam distillation are recommended to eliminate a mental block toward the use of such techniques. Experiments involving the above techniques will do much to broaden a student's background and training. The inclusion of experiments involving low and high pressure hydrogenation, the use of enzymes, and reactions on a micro scale, to mention a few, are also worthy projects.

In order to help the student decide how to run a reaction and isolate the products, the following outline is given.

Outline

Before carrying out any laboratory preparation, information on the following points is desirable.

A. A sound idea of the mechanism of the desired reaction and also the mechanisms of each reaction leading to undesirable side products should be gained.

This knowledge requires years of study but, for many reactions, mechanisms may be fairly well known and easily understood with little study. In particular it is important to know whether the ratio of products formed is governed by equilibria or rates. A sound theoretical background is very important in training a superior laboratory worker.

B. A knowledge of the different chemical methods available for carrying out the desired reaction.

It is very strongly recommended that students become familiar with the comprehensive treatise on organic chemistry by Houben-Weyl *Methoden der Organischen Chemie*, Georg Thieme Verlag, Stuttgart, Germany. Any student who has a rudimentary knowledge of German can make rapid headway with these volumes which contain invaluable information on different methods of carrying out transformations and syntheses. There are frequent explicit directions for performing reactions and numerous literature references.

In addition to the Houben-Weyl series, the yearly volumes by Thielheimer, *Synthetic Methods of Organic Chemistry*, S. Karger, Basel, Switzerland, are recommended as are the two volumes by Fieser and Fieser, *Reagents for Organic Synthesis*, Wiley-Interscience, New York. The above books provide a plentiful source of information of prime value to laboratory workers.

C. The effect of each variable on each of the competing reactions should be considered.

Before deciding how to run a reaction and isolate the product, balanced equations for each reaction which might occur should be written. In general attention should be given to running the reaction so that isolation of the products may be facilitated. Too often carrying out a reaction and isolation of the products are considered separately.

Several important variables are as follows.

1. Temperature

2. Concentration (many factors here including order of addition of reactants, amount of solvent, and so forth).
3. Solvent
4. Time of reaction
5. Choice of catalysts or other reagents.

D. Reactions should be run with high material balance.

Reaction conditions should be chosen with a view to separation and isolation of all products. To do this it is necessary to know the following.

1. Types of equipment available for various operations and advantages and limitations of each. Too often reactions or isolation procedures are carried out with poorly designed apparatus. Hence the accumulation of well-designed equipment is all important. Much of the apparatus involving standard taper joints seems designed to include as many glass joints as possible rather than to facilitate operations. It is advisable to become familiar with the series of books by Weissberger entitled *Technique of Organic Chemistry*, Interscience Publishers, Inc., New York, as there is comprehensive coverage of the types of apparatus used for all the common techniques used by organic chemists.
2. All expected products and their physical chemical properties. Here a knowledge of stability or tendency towards decomposition or polymerization is helpful. Familiarity with Hurd's *Pyrolysis of Carbon Compounds*, ACS monograph, is recommended.
3. When physical and when chemical methods are preferable as a means of separation.
4. When proper choice of solvent and reagent may significantly change ease of isolation, and so on.
5. How pure desired product must be.

Another aspect of experimentation which is emphasized in this course is the *time factor* in research. Many people think that the more time spent in the laboratory the better the student. I do not agree with this philosophy. University training should not only help graduate students to be better scientists but should also enable them to live fuller lives. Hence the important years spent in school should be used to develop interests other than chemistry. To have time available for other interests, a chemist must learn now to work *efficiently*. This means that the *time factor* must be considered in deciding how laboratory experiments should be run. While a student (or anyone else) is doing laboratory work, he should do this intently and not sit down to read the newspaper, a scientific journal, or enter into discussions about anything else. If a student learns how to work efficiently in the laboratory, more time will become available to spend in any way desired. Perhaps not many students are sufficiently motivated to exert this self-discipline, but a purpose is served by urging "while in the laboratory, do laboratory work!"

Techniques for carrying out certain operations vary greatly with regard to *working time* as compared to *elapsed time* from the start to the end of an experiment. Unless there is a reason to want a compound or result quickly, the working time is more important than the elapsed time. For example, a fairly water-soluble compound can often be effectively isolated by continuous ether extraction for a day. However, five manual extractions might yield 50% of the material present in an hour. A casual inspection of the above facts might suggest that less time is involved in the manual extraction technique. However, less *working time* is involved in continuous extraction and, in addition, a superior result is obtained. The important point is that during the hour used to do five manual extractions, *one would not be able to do anything else*. In contrast, setting up a continuous ether extraction apparatus takes only a few minutes (*provided the apparatus is readily available*). When the continuous extraction is completed, the entire product is in a relatively small amount of solvent, compared to the manual extraction volume, and can be worked up in a minimum of time.

The availability of apparatus, as mentioned above, is important. Often a research worker will say, when asked why such-and-such a technique was not used, "I didn't have the apparatus."

Assembly of well-designed apparatus is a must in performing superior laboratory work.

Neoprene stoppers instead of standard taper joints and flames instead of electric devices for heating are frequently recommended. The former make for greater ease of assembling multijointed setups, as greater flexibility is obtained. The latter is personal preference and need not be followed. However, the fear of fires is exaggerated.

Over the years, I cannot recall one fire caused by ignition of a volatile solvent by a flame in advanced laboratories under my supervision. There have been fires, but these usually result from improper disposal of dangerous reagents (for example, sodium or lithium aluminum hydride) or from having reactions get out of control.

Finally, a comment is in order about the enjoyment of laboratory work. If a laboratory worker does not take pride in accomplishment, much of the pleasure of laboratory work is lost. To develop a new reaction, to improve a yield or procedure, to devise a better piece of apparatus, even to obtain prettier and purer crystals, all of these are fun. I hope that the chemists of the future derive a lot of pleasure from their laboratory work.

One

Esterification of Adipic Acid

The primary objective of this experiment is to convert 50–100 g of adipic acid into diethyl adipate in a yield of at least 95%.

$$HOOC(CH_2)_4COOH + 2C_2H_5OH \overset{H^+}{\rightleftharpoons}$$

$$C_2H_5OOC(CH_2)_4COOC_2H_5 + 2H_2O$$

The techniques to be discussed involve the use of azeotropic distillation to drive a reaction to completion, quantitative transfer of material, liquid–liquid extraction in separatory funnels, and vacuum distillation.

Acid-catalyzed esterification is one of the most widely used reactions in organic chemistry [1]. The equation in general form is

$$RCOOH + R'OH \overset{H^+}{\rightleftharpoons} RCOOR' + H_2O$$

Only in cases in which R makes the rate of esterification extremely slow [2] or in which RCOOH or R'OH are sensitive to acid is there any difficulty in driving the esterification to completion.

The choice as to whether a methyl or an ethyl ester of an acid should be prepared is often unimportant because either is suitable for certain uses. However, certain features which demand consideration when planning an esterification should be mentioned. Methyl esters have higher melting points than ethyl esters in general. Hence, if purification is to be effected by crystallization, the methyl ester may be preferred. On the other hand, if distillation is to be used, the ethyl ester is preferable whenever the melting point of the methyl ester is high enough to cause solidification of the ester in the receiver (see page 36—discussion of apparatus). More subtle reasons for selection involve the ultimate use of the ester. If nuclear magnetic resonance (nmr) analysis of the product is desired, the use of methyl rather than ethyl is indicated. The greater simplicity of the signals for methyl esters provides for greater accuracy of results. The reasons for the choice of a particular alkyl group of an ester have by no means been exhausted, but the lesson to be learned is that some thought should be given to the next use of an ester before beginning an esterification.

There are two ways in which esterifications are usually run to completion.

1. Use of a large excess of alcohol
2. Removal of water

In the case of methanol a large excess of alcohol is most often used, whereas with ethanol removal of the water is superior.

1. Excess Alcohol (methyl esters)

In order to drive an esterification to completion by use of an excess of methanol, some idea of the value of the equilibrium constant of the reaction is desirable. Since the K_{eq} for most acids is about 4 and is little affected by the structure of R [3], about 26 moles of methanol (roughly one liter) is needed to insure that less than 1 % of acid remains in a 1-mole run. (About 6 moles of methanol (240 ml) is needed if 96 % of the ester is to be formed.) Thus, when the reaction mixture is worked up, a large amount of methanol must be removed. It is poor practice to remove this by distillation unless the acid catalyst is neutralized by addition of sodium carbonate.

The amount of strong acid used in esterification is often much greater than need be. In general 3–5 g of H_2SO_4 or toluene-sulfonic acid is ample for a 1-mole run. When the catalyst is to be neutralized during the workup, it is especially advantageous to use only a small amount.

As methanol is distilled the equilibrium is upset and moves toward increased concentration of organic acid, since water boils much higher than methanol (65°C). If the rate of hydrolysis of the ester is slow enough, such concentrations without neutralization of catalyst may not result in much hydrolysis, however, in general, neutralization is desirable. A simple alternate procedure involves the use of an insoluble strongly acid resin [4] as catalyst, since this may be easily removed by filtration. The filtrate can then be concentrated without fear of hydrolysis of ester and the residue processed as desired.

Esterification of an acid with methanol can be effected by the use of a "methyl ester column" described in Organic Synthesis, coll. vol. III, p. 610. *The use of acetone dimethyl ketal for scavenging water in the preparation of methyl esters is described in reference 4, pages 268–269.*

2. Removal of Water (ethyl esters)

Acids are readily converted into their ethyl esters by use of the *azeotropic method*. The success of this method depends upon the fact that water, ethanol, and benzene form a ternary azeotrope which boils at 64.4°C at 760 mm. On cooling, this azeotrope separates into two liquid phases: the upper one consisting of about 86 % benzene, 13 % ethanol, and 1 % water; the lower phase con-

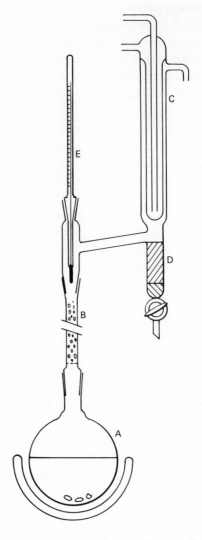

Figure 1-1. Phase separating head for esterifications.

sisting of about 5% benzene, 52% ethanol, and 43% water. By means of a suitable technique the water formed in the esterification can be efficiently removed (see Figure 1–1).

The principle involved is that of the Dean–Stark trap [5].

A solution of the acid to be esterified in ethanol and benzene, together with acid catalyst and some boiling stones, is placed in flask A, the fractionation column B is put in place and the phase-separating head C attached. On distillation through B, fractionation is effected and the ternary azeotrope of benzene-alcohol-water (bp 64.6°C) is liquified at the condenser C and collects in the chamber D in which it separates into two layers.

This experiment does not require an extremely efficient column. For example, a 1.5-ft section packed with 1/4-in. glass helices or glass beads is ample. The column need not be insulated.

When D is filled, the upper layer overflows and is recycled to B. The lower layer may be tapped off from time to time if the size of the run produces too much lower layer to be collected in D. As the removal of water nears completion, the temperature noted at thermometer E rises because the column is unable to perform the fractionation necessary to yield the ternary azeotrope.

The incorporation of a thermometer at E is not necessary. When small droplets of the heavier phase cease to form, most of the water has been removed from the reaction mixture.

In a fairly short time the temperature rises to 67.8°C, the boiling point of the binary azeotrope of alcohol–benzene (45 mole % ethanol). It is desirable to remove the lower layer from D completely at this point.

Strict reliance on temperature as a guide to completion of reaction is not necessary or desirable. If the amounts of benzene and alcohol used initially have been thought out, most of the excess alcohol can be removed by distillation of the binary azeotrope and thus make it easier to work up the product.

The reaction mixture is now ready to be worked up. Depending on the ester, different procedures may be chosen. However, in most cases the procedure described next is recommended (see Figure 1–2).

The contents of the flask A are transferred quantitatively to a separatory funnel B containing sufficient sodium carbonate solution D to neutralize the catalyst and any acid which has not been esterified (usually less than 1 %). Because the quantitative transfer of solutions

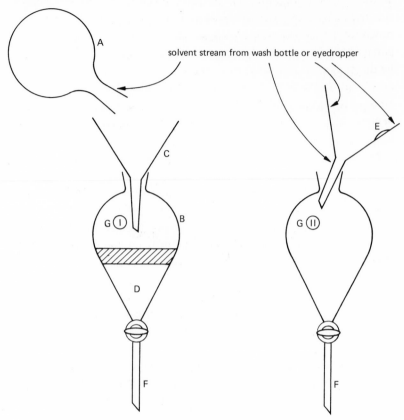

Figure 1-2. Extractions using separatory funnels.

is basic to many operations, space will be devoted here to a discussion of this technique.

Quantitative Transfer of Solutions

In transferring the solution from A to the separatory funnel B, a funnel C should be used. It is quite difficult to pour through the mouth of the separatory funnel without such an aid. When the flask A has been emptied, the outside of the neck portion of the flask should be rinsed off with solvent *while still upside down* (see Figure 1-2). This prevents the small amount of solution which has crept over the edge from running down the outside of A when the flask is returned to an upright position. The solution inside A is then rinsed down with additional solvent, and the transfer of this solution to B repeated as just described until it is certain that no appreciable amount of material remains in the flask. After each transfer the outside neck of A is washed with solvent. Finally the funnel C is washed down from the top and later the outside. When washing an oily or partly crystalline material from a surface, the solvent stream should be directed well *above* that material, E, so that it will all be washed down into the desired receiver. If solvent is directed at E, a certain amount of the material will creep *upwards* over the edge of the funnel. Whenever this happens it is much more difficult to transfer without loss.

For rinsing with solvent a plastic wash bottle is recommended. However, if the hole in the exit tube is too large, much larger amounts of solvent are used than are necessary. In small-scale runs, rinsing off with an eyedropper in which the opening has been made small by melting the conventional tube is useful. The transfer operation is now complete. Similar techniques apply to almost all transfer operations.

These directions may seem trivial to many but it is strongly recommended that they be followed for the following reasons. By avoiding the contamination of the outside of apparatus, contact of chemicals with the skin is avoided. This decreases the probability of becoming allergic to the chemicals. Occasionally, students have had to stop working with the chemicals involved in their research because of the advent of severe skin disorders. Other less serious cases have been encountered. Very little more solvent or time is needed to rinse the outside of the equipment, and there is no loss of material. Time is saved in cleaning apparatus as both the inside and the outside of the flask are almost completely clean.

For most operations the solvent recommended is a mixture of ether and benzene (approximately 1:1). Such a solvent is preferable to benzene or ether alone for the following reasons.

1. The viscosity of the mixture is less than that of benzene alone; hence the solvent wets the glass more easily and washes off material more completely.
2. When the mixed solvent is finally removed, the distillation of benzene automatically dries the solution unless a very hygroscopic material is at hand.

Extractions in which the nonaqueous layer containing the desired product is at the top are easier to process because the main layer containing most of the product remains in the separatory funnel at all times.

General Extraction Procedure

To carry out liquid–liquid extraction in the best way, the use of two pear-shaped separatory funnels, each of which is modified slightly as shown in Figure 1-2, is recommended.

The stem is cut off at an angle at F so that it is only about 3–4 in. long. If the funnels purchased (usually pairs of 250-, 500-, and 1000-ml sizes are most useful) do not have etched circles G on which notation I or II can be made; the stems should be cut to different lengths so that the funnels can be identified. The reason for this is that glass joints which have been ground-in fit better than do commerical 𝕋 items. By having a better fit the use of grease to lubricate the stopcocks and stoppers may be avoided, but ground-in stopcocks are no longer interchangeable.

Although interchangeable 𝕋 stopcocks and plugs are routinely available often the fit is not as good as desirable. In order to make a better fit the stopcock (or plug) is treated with a slurry of carborundum powder (size 3/F) and water held in the palm of the hand. The stopcock is then ground into the bore with a twisting motion until a much better fit is attained. This operation requires only a few minutes. The 𝕋 feature is thus modified sufficiently so that each ground-in stopcock should be labeled I or II by using a marking pencil on the rough end of the stopcock. The marking will ensure that stopcock I (and plug I) will be used with separatory funnel I, and so on, each time. These stopcocks and plugs are then used without grease. A little water is applied as lubricant. Care must be taken to push in the stopcock just the right amount. A "feel" is acquired in a short time. If pushed in too hard the stopcock will stick; if too easily, leakage will occur. The use of more expensive Teflon stopcocks is increasing but is not recommended. One must be careful to prevent a piece of hard solid, such as sand or broken glass, from getting into the plug because, on turning, the Teflon becomes scored and thereafter a leak may develop.

A common problem in vacuum distillation arises from foaming (see page 25) often caused by the silicones used as lubricants on stopcocks and stoppers. These silicones partly dissolve in the organic layer during the extraction process.

*A water-soluble stopcock grease is described by C. C. Meloche and W. G. Fredrick, J. Amer. Chem. Soc., **54**, 3264 (1932). This grease is not recommended for stopcocks where aqueous solutions are involved, but is advantageous in many other cases.*

The separatory funnel containing the carbonate solution and reaction mixture is now shaken *gently* with the stopcock end pointing up, and the stopcock is opened *immediately* to relieve any pressure. The stopper should be held firmly as the pressure produced due to the formation of carbon dioxide may force out this plug, with resultant loss of material. The process of shaking and release of pressure should be repeated until equilibrium has been reached (as indicated by the lack of any hiss when the stopcock is opened). The separatory funnel, after a slight swirling motion in an upright position, should then be placed on the ring support; the stopper should be removed and rinsed with ether–benzene, and the funnel allowed to stand until the layers have separated.

Circular ring supports without inward protruding points are recommended. These supports should be wrapped with thin asbestos tape to insure against breakage of separatory funnels which can occur if they are set down too roughly on unprotected rings.

If the layers do not separate well in a short time, the reason should be determined. Sometimes the densities of the organic and aqueous phases are too nearly the same. In this case one can add more ether to the upper layer, some saturated salt solution to the bottom layer, or both. More often the trouble is due to the presence of insoluble matter at the interface. In this case the entire contents should be filtered into the second separatory funnel. All surfaces should be washed well with solvent as previously described. Since suction filtration is necessary, the use of the adapter and setup shown in Figure 1-3 saves a transfer of liquid from a suction flask to the separatory funnel. The use of a layer of filter aid at A is recommended.

Celite and Super-cell, Johns-Manville Co., are satisfactory.

If only a filter paper is used on the Buchner funnel B, it often becomes clogged with the offending solid. The adapter C is fitted by a suitable stopper D to the receiver E, in this case the second separatory funnel indicated in Figure 1-2. The distance from the end of the delivery

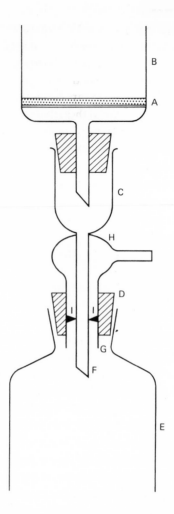

Figure 1-3. Suction filtration adapter.

tube F to the bottom of the adapter G is important. About 1/2 in. is recommended. If longer, the leverage on the end F to the seal H is increased, and an accidental push will cause breakage at H. If too short, liquid emerging at F will be sucked up into the adapter. Three evenly spaced glass protrusions I which just touch the inner wall of G are important in decreasing breakage at H. Once the pressure differential between the interior of E and the atmosphere has been established so that the rate of filtration is suitable, the system should be cut off from the aspirator by manipulation of a stopcock (see page 47). Too large a pressure differential will cause boiling of the filtrate in E. After the main batch of reaction mixture has been filtered into E, the usual washings should be carried out both with ether–benzene and with an aqueous phase similar to that present in the mixture.

The extraction procedure may then be continued with assurance that separation of layers will be rapid. The aqueous phase from one separatory funnel is tapped into the other separatory funnel and reextracted with ether–benzene. The lower phase from this funnel is then tapped into a suitable size Erlenmeyer flask (hereinafter called E flask) and the upper layer returned to the first funnel, all transfers being made quantitatively. The aqueous phase in the E flask can then be reextracted in a separatory funnel as many times as experience shows necessary.

The greater the amount of water-soluble reaction solvent (in the present case, alcohol, but often water-miscible solvents, such as dioxane, tetrahydrofuran, dimethylformamide, and many others) present when the reaction mixture is submitted to workup, the greater the loss of product in the aqueous phase unless multiple reextractions are carried out. *When working with valuable materials never throw anything away until the products have been accounted for.*

The combined organic phase should now be extracted with more water and the water layer again reextracted with ether–benzene. After a sufficient number of water washings have been carried out to ensure removal of inorganic constituents, catalysts, and so on, the organic layer should be extracted with alkali to remove acidic substances (unreacted organic acid in this case). Again each alkaline wash should be reextracted with ether–benzene and this extract returned to the funnel. If a basic substance is to be removed, washes with aqueous acid are indicated. The last traces of magnesium halides from Grignard reactions or aluminum salts from Friedel-Crafts reactions should be carefully removed with acid washes because of troubles such traces might cause in subsequent distillation of reaction products (see page 35 under distillation).

The organic layer should then be washed with a saturated salt solution.

It is convenient to keep a large bottle filled with such a solution as a fairly long time is needed to produce a saturated solution.

This wash reduces markedly the aqueous content of the organic layer, which should then be filtered through a cone of anhydrous magnesium sulfate A as shown in Figure 1-4. The amount of

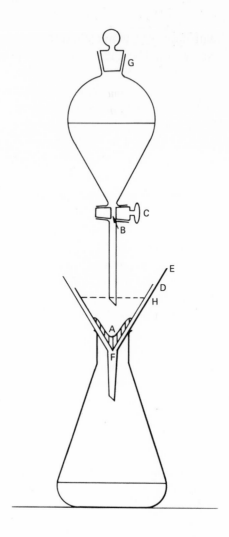

Figure 1-4. Filtration of organic layer through drying agents.

magnesium sulfate should be kept at a minimum to prevent loss of material, since it is difficult to wash thoroughly, and to expedite the rate of filtration. The amount can be decreased markedly if the aqueous phase B remaining in the bore of the stopcock C is allowed to drain out and be displaced by the ether–benzene layer before placing the funnel and receiver in place.

The technique used in this filtration varies with the size of the run and the nature of the solute. The filter paper, the top edge of which at D should be *at least* 1/2 in. from the top of the funnel E, should be of a porous grade (Reeve–Angel 902 is suitable) so that the rate of flow is rapid.

Attention should be paid to the amount of overlap in folding the filter paper so that the cone formed has an internal angle at the apex F that is slightly greater than the similar angle of the funnel. Careful attention to this detail will ensure a faster rate of filtration and make it easier to wash down all of the products at the end.

In small runs the rate is governed by the manipulation of stop-cock C. In large runs it is too time-consuming to bother with attention to the stopcock. Rather, a stopper at G is put in firmly and the stopcock C opened wide. The level H of the solution in the funnel is governed by placement of the tip of the separatory funnel since air can enter the latter only through this tip. When all of the solution has passed through, careful washing with ether–benzene should be carried out. The solvent should always be directed at the top of the funnel, well above the oily or solid layer produced just above the edge of the filter paper by evaporation during the filtration process.

If a material tends to crystallize or separate as a viscous layer at the rim of the filter paper, or just above this on the funnel, during the filtration, one should rinse with solvent frequently in order to prevent a buildup of material. Otherwise much more solvent (and time) may be needed to rinse it down later.

The greatest loss of material in such filtrations occurs at the folds of the filter paper (as can be seen by drying and noting where the colored areas are). Hence, although fluted filters are widely suggested, their use should be avoided as they are more difficult to wash thoroughly. The solution in the E flask is now ready for further treatment.

The acidic portion of the reaction products, if any, is recoverable by a similar extraction technique from the alkaline washings (see page 14) after acidification. The basic component of the reaction mixture is similarly recoverable from the acid washing (see page 14) after making basic. Thus, any reaction mixture can be almost quantitatively separated into neutral, acid, and basic fractions as described. The isolation of pure products from these fractions depends on the nature of the components.

The next phase in the workup is removal of the ether–benzene solvent prior to further treatment. This is accomplished under atmospheric or reduced pressure, depending on the situation. Most often atmospheric distillation is convenient and economical. However, there is a growing tendency towards the use of rotary evaporators. Because good rotary evaporators are expensive, it is assumed that these will not generally be available in a laboratory course. Whenever the compounds to be isolated are sensitive to heat, obviously the solvent should be removed under reduced pressure. If atmospheric distillation is used, the apparatus shown in Figure 1-5 is recommended.

The reflux-distillation condenser A held by clamp B is an extremely useful piece of apparatus.

This design was originated by Dr. E. B. Hershberg at Harvard in 1935.

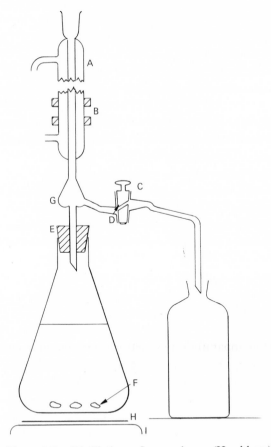

Figure 1-5. Distillation-reflux condenser (Hershberg).

By merely turning the slanting-bore stopcock C to the position shown, the operation can be changed from refluxing to distilling. The slanting-bore feature creates a small vapor lock at D which allows this condenser to be used even for distillation of low-boiling solvents. An important feature of this setup has to do with the cork E. A series of different size corks which will fit E flasks of 125–1000-ml capacity should be prepared. After being sure that the corks are well bored so that they fit the condenser properly, they are flamed gently so that the entire outside part, which is to come in contact with the flask, is slightly charred. The charred part is then rubbed gently to remove loose particles. A cork so prepared will hold a full E flask firmly without other support so that the flask may be held above, and not resting on, the surface of the hot plate. With a little practice one can easily determine just how hard the flask must be pushed, with a slightly twisting motion, so that it will not come off easily.

In my experience I have never had a flask fall off of the condenser when left above the hot plate as shown.

With this setup a great deal of flexibility in the rate of distillation can be attained by paying attention to two variables, the temperature of the hot plate and the distance the flask is held from the surface of the hot plate. This distance is easily changed by loosening the clamp B and raising or lowering the condenser A. If, for example, one must be away from the laboratory for a period of time (say—for lunch or a class) solvent can still be distilled safely without fear that the residue will be overheated. Merely adjust the position of the flask over the hot plate. If ⸸ joints are used on the condenser A, it is not safe to suspend the flask above the hot plate unless the flask is also clamped.

Where extremely pure products are desired ⸸ joints are preferable because small amounts of impurities are extracted from corks or neoprene stoppers by hot solvents.

In using this apparatus three safety features should be emphasized. If the boiling chips F are forgotten, never add them while the solution is hot (superheated) because the resulting ebullition might cause a severe accident. The solvent–air mixture might ignite from the hot plate or a neighboring flame. Even if no fire results, much material may be lost. Boiling chips remaining in a solution which has been at reflux and cooled are not always effective, if the solution is again heated to reflux. Always put in new boiling chips when a solution is heated to reflux. Secondly, never use the stopcock sidearm as a lever to loosen the condenser from the cork. Breakage can cause severe hand cuts. Even if the sidearm does not break off, a crack may develop in the circular part G. The latter should be made strong so that breakage at this point is minimized. Finally, a circular sheet of asbestos paper H or several strips should be placed on the hot plate I to minimize the chance of breakage when a flask is placed on the hot plate.

When most of the solvent has been removed, the remaining solution is ready for further processing. In the present case vacuum distillation is employed.

The recovered solvent may be used for other extractions.

Vacuum Distillation

Whenever vacuum distillation is to be used in an isolation or purification scheme, a clear idea is necessary as to whether distillation or fractional distillation is desired. Often, a good deal of time and material is lost because the objective of the distillation is not clearly in mind. In the present case we can assume that the adipic acid used in the preparation of the ester is pure. Hence the only purpose of the distillation is to remove the last traces of solvent and any colored nonvolatile impurities that might be present because of slight impurities in any reagent used or in the starting acid. Such a distillation might be called an *upward filtration*.

The apparatus suggested is shown in Figure 1-6. As there are several features concerning distillation that deserve discussion, these will be taken up under separate headings. Furthermore, the discussions will be concerned mainly with distillations in which appreciable amounts of products are concerned, for example, 50–1000 g quantities. When smaller quantities are to be distilled, different techniques may be desirable. If the recommended techniques are followed, a laboratory worker will be able to carry out other operations while the distillation is proceeding almost without attention.

There are several different ways to supply the heat needed for a vacuum distillation. For amounts of 1–50 g of materials boiling below about 150°C at the pressure involved, heating with a gas burner is most often to be preferred. For larger amounts, and for

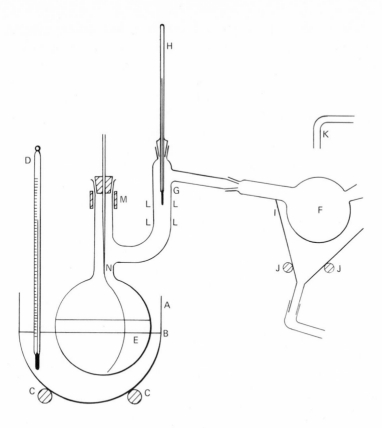

Figure 1-6. Set up for vacuum distillation.

small runs of high-boiling substances, heating by means of a bath A is recommended. Heating of the bath may be effected by means of a gas burner of the Tirrill or Fletcher type (which are controlled by regulation of a needle valve) or by an electric heating mantle. One advantage of heating by a gas flame (besides the lower cost of equipment) is that the temperature of the bath can be changed more rapidly than with electric mantles. Either technique is satisfactory when experience is gained. The important points are to maintain careful control of the temperature of the heating bath and to be able to arrive at the desired temperature rapidly. Small differences in the amount of heat being introduced into the pot (the term used for the part of any apparatus in which the distilland is held) can be effected by adjusting the level B of the heating liquid in the bath by changing the position of the bath support C.

When an electric heating mantle is used, raising and lowering of the bath can be easily effected with the aid of a lab jack placed under the heating mantle.

Glycerine is useful as a material for heating baths for bath temperatures recorded by thermometer D up to about 140°C. If a good grade of anhydrous glycerine is used, such temperatures are held without excessive decomposition. When glycerine baths are used beakers are preferable as bath vessels so that after use the glycerine may be poured while still warm into a glass-stoppered bottle for storage because glycerine is quite hygroscopic. Air baths are also often useful.

For heating at temperatures up to 300°C a potassium nitrate–sodium nitrite (10:7 by weight) mixture, which melts at about 145°C, is recommended. For higher temperatures a potassium nitrate–sodium nitrate (1:1) mixture may be used. The fused-salt baths have the advantages listed.

1. Flames can be played over their surfaces (see page 25) without danger of fire.
2. They remain almost colorless after long use, whereas organic liquids invariably discolor.
3. They are water soluble and hence easily washed from apparatus.
4. They make for cleaner desks as there is no oiliness such as accumulates near oil baths.

The main disadvantages are as follows: the mixtures are hygroscopic so that in humid weather covers are needed; they must be melted before a flask can be inserted; and metal containers, which eliminate visibility in certain directions, must be used. However, stainless steel kitchen bowls of various sizes are readily available.

In carrying out distillation with the apparatus shown in Figure 1-6 the following points are of importance.

1. Small amounts of solvent remain in the liquid E to be distilled. Most of this can be removed at atmospheric pressure while the temperature of the bath is being raised. However, small amounts of solvent remain until the liquid begins to boil under reduced pressure. In practice when the mixture first boils under vacuum there is a rapid loss of this solvent (sometimes with frothing) which can be troublesome. Use

a temporary receiver F until the liquid to be distilled is refluxing at G. The heat input is easily regulated by control of the temperature and the level of the heating medium at B. There is no one ideal differential between the temperature of the heating bath and the boiling point (indicated at thermometer H). The amount of contact between the heating liquid and flask can be varied easily by raising or lowering the heating bath or the flask. The flexibility of apparatus necessary if one is to raise or lower the flask and the attached receiver is provided for in part by the nature of the support of the receiver F. There should be no fixed clamp on the neck of this receiver—rather support should be obtained from the rim of the funnel I which is held in place by support ring J. By tilting the funnel I properly F can readily be supported when the flask is raised or lowered moderate distances. The funnel I thus plays a dual role: it supports receiver F and carries off cooling water played on the receiver from the outlet K.

2. When the vacuum is broken so that a receiver may be changed, the level of the heating medium should be lowered. This ensures that little heat is added to the flask contents while the change is being made. If this precaution is not taken, ebullition is too rapid when vacuum is reapplied and liquid may be carried over mechanically. Even if the latter does not occur, the boiling point of the liquid which is distilled in the rapid ebullition phase is not known.

3. At the start of vacuum distillation there is often foaming, which can be very annoying as liquid is carried over mechanically and must be returned to the pot. As this operation is time-consuming, the foaming must be eliminated. This can often be accomplished by directing the flame of a burner at the region L on the neck of the Claisen flask *before* the frothing reaches this point. When the froth reaches this hot region it collapses (hopefully), and a small amount of material is flash distilled. This portion may either be retained in the receiver in use or, when frothing has ceased, the receiver F may be changed. This procedure is continued for as long as necessary. However, if serious frothing continues after the above technique has been tried for a short time, it is usually best not to waste more time. Rather, the entire contents of the flask may be stirred with some de-

colorizing carbon and filtered, using the setup shown in Figure 1-3, into another Claisen flask without washing the filter cake with solvent. Hopefully this treatment will preferentially remove (or decrease the amount of) the offending foaming agent and distillation may be effected. The silicones used as stopcock lubricants may be the culprit—hence, the preference for using separatory funnels whose stopcocks are not lubricated.

In a vacuum distillation the pressure should be kept constant. In general it is convenient to use whatever pressure a conventional system (see Figure 1-7) will produce, unless the boiling point is so low that complete condensation is difficult. In such cases, the distillation setup can be modified to include a water-cooled condenser (which need not be longer than 9 in. overall, joints included) before the receiver. Alternatively, the pressure regulator in the system may be used to raise the pressure and, hence, the boiling point. In a good system the pressure should be 1 mm or less. If the pump will not provide such a pressure, an oil change may be necessary or repair of the pump may be needed.

There is some difference of opinion on how a vacuum system should be set up. The one illustrated in Figure 1-7 represents a typical, but not unique, arrangement.

For use in a laboratory course more than one vacuum system should be made available on movable carts. In a research laboratory the apparatus is arranged at a permanent location.

When assembling a vacuum system, all pressure tubing should be cleaned internally by careful washing if examination shows that the inside is coated with a powdery substance. The washing is effected by pouring a solution of sodium phosphate–Alconox (a commercial detergent) (1 : 2) through a funnel attached at one end of the tubing

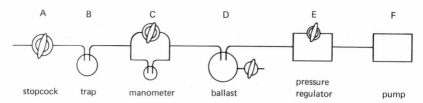

Figure 1-7. Vacuum system.

and collecting the solution in a beaker. This process should be repeated several times. After thorough rinsing and drying the tubing is ready for use.

The glass tubing used to make connections should be large enough that a close, tight fit is maintained but not so large that the rubber tubing is stretched too much. Such stretching accelerates cracking of the rubber tubing. Whenever a glass-to-rubber tubing connection is to be made or broken, use glycerine as a lubricant. This is conveniently applied when removing a piece of rubber tubing from a glass connection by inserting a thin, flattened metal object moistened with glycerine between the two and working this around the tube. The handle end of a small iron file, ground to appropriate size and shape, makes a convenient tool. The end should not be sharp in order to avoid cutting the rubber tubing. A lot of broken apparatus and cut hands would be avoided if glycerine lubrication were used routinely.

A stopcock, firmly clamped so that the plug can be turned with one hand, at A (Figure 1-7) is useful for the following reasons: to prevent access of air to the liquid remaining in the pot while still hot after certain distillations have been completed; to allow for introduction of an inert gas when desirable; and to cut off the vacuum system rapidly without breaking the vacuum suddenly, as occasionally is required to avoid too rapid ebullition or foaming.

A trap B can be placed at almost any position in the vacuum train. When placed as shown in the general scheme illustrated in Figure 1-7, the remaining items in the train are protected from various vapors. The trap B should be connected as shown in Figure 1-8 so that the wide interior is connected to the distillation side of the system and the narrow exit tube is connected to the pump side. Occasionally solvent (especially benzene and *t*-butyl alcohol) solidifies on coming in contact with the trap. If this solidification occurs in the narrow tube, the system is easily blocked. There is much more leeway if solidification occurs on the wide part. The trap B is held in proper position in the Dewar flask c by the clamp d. The cooling bath e is prepared by adding dry ice to isopropyl alcohol, which is preferable to other solvents because foaming on the addition of the dry ice is more easily controlled.

Do not use so much dry ice that, if the trap B is removed for inspection or to allow frozen solvent to melt and flow to the bottom, it is difficult to return the trap to its original position.

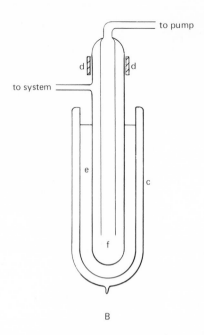

Figure 1-8. Vacuum trap.

A fair amount of space f should be available in the trap for collection of solvent or low-boiling materials below the inner tube end, as shown. If sensitive compounds are to be distilled, one may not wish to break the vacuum after the solvent is removed. The space f can be used to catch the solvent, and vacuum distillation can be carried out without interruption. After distillation, stopcock A of Figure 1-7 may be closed, the pump section disconnected, and nitrogen or other inert gas introduced through A.

For a manometer (C of Figure 1-7) the Zimmerli gauge (see Figure 1-9) is preferred, because it is so easily cleaned and filled. To place a Zimmerli gauge in operation (or to clean a dirty one) the stopcock A should be thoroughly cleaned so that no trace of stopcock grease remains. The interior of the gauge is cleaned by treating with cleaning solution (sodium dichromate in warm concentrated sulfuric acid) followed by treating with a warm solution prepared by dissolving a *small* amount (about 50–100 mg) of powdered potassium permanganate in concentrated sulfuric acid. This solution is a dangerous and powerful oxidizing solution. *It should never be used when more than traces of organic matter are on the surface of the object to be cleaned.* However, the solution is extremely effective in

An Advanced Organic Laboratory Course

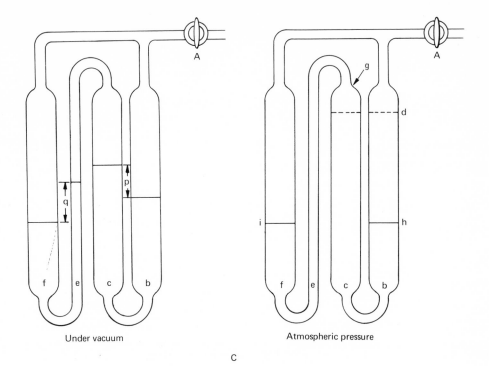

Under vacuum   Atmospheric pressure

c

Figure 1-9. Zimmerli gauge.

removing such traces from glass surfaces and will do so rapidly. The solutions above described are readily introduced into the gauge by applying a water pump vacuum to the system and closing stopcock A. The tip is then placed under the surface of the cleaning solution and the stopcock is opened, whereupon the solution is sucked into the gauge. Most of the solution can be poured out after use and water or other rinsing solutions sucked in, and so on.

The sulfuric acid solutions should always be introduced into and removed from the gauge when at room temperature. Heating is carried out after the solutions have been introduced into the gauge.

The clean, dry gauge is then evacuated, and sufficient *clean* mercury is sucked in to reach height d when it is all collected in tubes b and c. Tilt the apparatus so that the mercury column rises in c and the mercury will pour from c through the narrow column e into f. When a small amount of mercury has flowed into f (without trapping any air at point g) the gauge is rapidly tilted back to an upright position.

The attention of the glass blower who is to make this gauge should be called to the danger of trapping air at point g. The glass construction from the large to the small tubing should be such that no air will be trapped at g when properly tilted.

The mercury should now form a continuous liquid column from h in b to i in f. The stopcock A can now be greased (avoid an excess).

When the gauge is connected to an evacuated system, the mercury in tubes b and f will rise until there is a break in the column (in tubes e or c). The difference p in the heights of mercury in b and c then measures the pressure in the system because the pressure in the interior tube c (and e) is merely that of mercury at room temperature. The height p is read directly on a strip of millimeter paper attached to the wooden stand used to support the gauge. The height q between the columns of mercury in tubes e and f should not be taken as the pressure because there is a difference in the diameter of tubes e and f; hence, this height is not as accurate a measure of the pressure as p. The reason for ensuring that no air is trapped at g during the filling operation is now clear. Any gas so trapped would make the pressures in the tubes e and c (under vacuum situation) greater than the pressure of mercury and hence would cause the pressure read to be less than the true pressure.

If pressures lower than 1 mm are involved McLeod gauges must be used.

Consult apparatus catalogs for gauges of various kinds, including Zimmerli and McLeod types.

For general use in vacuum distillation pressures of about 1 mm are attained if there are only very small leaks in the setup and the vacuum pump is operating well. If pressures somewhat higher than 1 mm are desired, a pressure regulator E (Figure 1-7) is required. A convenient device [6] is shown in Figure 1-10.

In use stopcock c should be left open until the pressure is slightly higher than the final operating pressure desired (usually from 6 to 10 mm if ethyl phthalate is used as the liquid in the pressure regulator). The stopcock is then closed and the system allowed to come to the pressure determined by the height of the liquid at h.

Since ethyl phthalate has a density of about 1, and mercury about 13.5, a height of 13.5 millimeters of ethyl phthalate is needed for each millimeter of mercury.

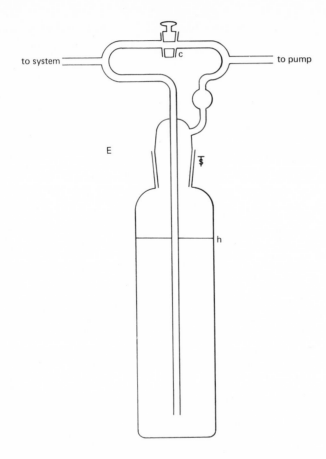

to system

to pump

c

E

h

Figure 1-10. Newman pressure regulator.

When distillation has been completed and it is necessary to release the vacuum, it is important first to shut the stopcock A (in Figure 1-7) in the vacuum system, then open stopcock c on the pressure regulator E and slowly admit air into the system through stopcock e in the ballast flask D, Figure 1-11. This procedure avoids loss of liquid from the pressure regulator.

Another simple device for pressure regulation employs the needle valve of a Fletcher or Tirrill type of gas burner connected by a T-tube to the vacuum system. The amount of leakage through the needle valve regulates the pressure. For use over a long time this device

If a needle valve leak is used, the Newman pressure regulator E should be replaced by the leak regulator.

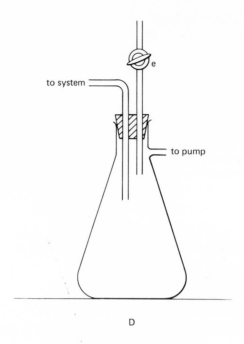

Figure 1-11. Ballast flask.

may not work well if a piece of lint or other solid lodges at the air intake. The leak will thus be decreased and the pressure in the system will drop.

A large empty flask D to act as ballast should be included in order to decrease the rate of pressure change in the system and thus to ensure easier control. A 2-liter suction flask (see Figure 1-11) is satisfactory. The stopper at the top should include stopcock e in order that the system may be readily connected to (or shut off from) the atmosphere.

For most vacuum distillation the type of Claisen flask shown in Figure 1-6 is recommended. The thermometer is of the type that has a 3-in. extension to the mercury bulb. The sidearm consists of a 14/35 ⊤ inside joint. The overall length of the sidearm varies with the size of the flask. It is better to have the take-off sidearm $1-1\frac{1}{2}$ in. above the thermometer bulb (see the section on Vacuum Distillation Technique for the reason). The flask should be clamped as shown at M (Figure 1-6) with asbestos tape between the clamp and the flask.

A number of clamps wrapped with asbestos should be prepared for varied uses. Asbestos is preferable to rubber or plastic since it can be strongly heated if desired, whereas rubber- or plastic-coated clamps should not.

Clamps used to hold Claisen flasks should have some compressible material at the glass–metal contact. If they do not, cracks often develop in the glass neck because the expansion of glass on heating causes undue strain to develop. Since the clamp at M is the only fixed firm support for the distilling flask and receiver, this contact should be firm but not unyielding.

The receivers F are round-bottomed flasks of various size to which outside 14/35 ⚓ joints are sealed as shown in Figure 1-6.

Vacuum Distillation Technique

This description of distillation technique is general and applies to vacuum distillation of crude reaction mixtures as well as to a relatively pure substance as in the case of diethyl adipate.

When the apparatus described in the preceding section and the solution containing the material to be distilled are assembled, vacuum distillation may be started. Emphasis should be placed on the term distillation as opposed to fractionation, for in the latter case (see page 86) different apparatus is recommended.

The liquid to be distilled (in the present case diethyl adipate) is transferred to the Claisen flask quantitatively, a boiling stone added, and most of the solvent removed by appropriate heating while the bath is being brought to the temperature needed for the vacuum distillation. The receiver is cooled by tap water during this period. The application of suction by a water aspirator at the end of this preliminary heating period removes all but the small amount of solvent dissolved in the material to be distilled. To try to remove this solvent by prolonged aspiration and heating is pointless. The loss of this dissolved solvent is diffusion controlled and, hence, very slow unless the surface of the liquid is continuously renewed by mechanical stirring.

When all but the dissolved solvent has been removed, a new receiver is attached and capillary tube N (Figure 1-6) put in place. Instead of a capillary (for construction see page 83) various types of commercially available boiling stones or wooden applicator sticks (less desirable) may be used. On occasion magnetically driven stirrers can be used to ensure smooth ebullition.

The vacuum system described in Figure 1-7 is connected, and a portable plastic shield is placed to protect the operator. The drop in pressure is controlled by manipulation of the stopcock at A to be sure that the liquid in the flask does not boil too rapidly if it has been overheated. When the liquid first boils under reduced pressure, the dissolved solvent will suddenly be lost. A certain amount of skill is needed in approaching this point so that liquid will not mechanically bump over into the receiver.

When the pressure on the manometer C (Figure 1-7) reaches the desired value, the heating should be controlled so that ebullition begins at a slow rate. The variables involved are the temperature of the heating bath and the level of the heating fluid. The important point to observe, if a large quantity of material is to be distilled with a minimum of attention, is that the heat input must be regulated so that the rate of distillation is not too slow or too rapid. At the start the distillation rate should be controlled so that the ring of condensing liquid rises in the neck of the Claisen flask up to a point G (Figure 1-6) just above the thermometer bulb but not so high as to effect distillation of much product.

If the thermometer bulb is directly opposite the take-off point quite a few milliliters of product are distilled before thermal equilibrium is reached and it is impossible to know if a lower boiling fraction is involved or not. A hollow stem thermometer is slightly preferable to a solid stem thermometer because it approaches thermal equilibrium more rapidly.

This technique allows the boiling point of the first portion to be determined, as time is needed for thermal equilibrium to be reached. After such equilibrium is attained, only a little more heat input will ensure steady distillation until almost all of the product has distilled. If more heat is applied than is needed to attain a reasonable rate of distillation, the temperature of distillation will go up a number of degrees.

The reason for the rise in the temperature of distillation is that the pressure which obtains at the thermometer bulb is higher than that recorded at the manometer which remains essentially unchanged. The pressure increase is due to the greatly increased vapor flow (caused by too large input of heat) for the diameter of the takeoff sidearm.

In itself this is no drawback and may be desirable in order to decrease the time needed for distillation. If increased entrainment due to increased rate of ebullition causes the color of the distillate to darken, the rate can be decreased.

When a gas bubble bursts, a small droplet of liquid is propelled up into the vapor stream. Entrainment is the phenomenon by which such droplets of liquid are mechanically carried over in the vapor.

When almost all of the liquid has been distilled trouble may arise if peroxides and Lewis acid type halides, such as magnesium bromide of aluminum chloride, have not been thoroughly removed from the product being distilled. Because most of the organic product has been distilled, the concentration of the offending impurity will have increased greatly. If this concentration becomes high enough, a violent exothermic decomposition reaction may occur. The exothermic decomposition may be merely annoying, if mild enough so that only a little dark-colored material distills into the collected product; however, it may be violent enough to cause a small explosion. Usually a change in the sound of the operation of the vacuum pump can be detected just before such a decomposition occurs. At the first change in sound, stop the distillation using safety gloves. A shield should always be placed in front of a vacuum distillation for safety. Safety goggles must always be worn.

The last amount of product which wets the necks and walls of the distillation flask may be caused to distill by flaming with a bunsen burner (or heating with an infrared heat lamp). The flame is played lightly over the entire part of the Claisen flask above the heating liquid, so that condensation on the walls does not occur, and the last small amounts of liquid may be distilled.

The flaming of the Claisen flask is one reason why nonflammable liquid baths are preferable to oil baths.

The heating should not be so strong as to cause distillation of a higher-boiling component, should one be present, but just strong enough so that condensation on the walls does not cause loss of product.

The objection may be raised that one should not flame the Claisen flask because the boiling point of the portion distilled in this way is unknown. However, with vapor phase chromatography (vpc) to check purity of product this objection is met. The lower yield obtained if the flask is not flamed almost always makes this feature worthwhile. If extreme purity is desired for any reason, the entire product should be redistilled, preferably in a fractionating column.

If the distillate is a solid, it may solidify in the sidearm of the receiver and cause trouble by sealing off the flask section. Whenever the problem of solidification arises, suitable adjustment of a small flame from a burner or proper placement of an infrared heat lamp will keep the distillate from solidifying until it reaches the main part of the receiver.

This description covers the process of distillation of reasonably large amounts of product in such a way that a minimum of attention need be paid to the process while the main quantity is being distilled; hence, other operations can be carried out at the same time.

If one wishes to do only a distillation and not try to do anything else at the same time, or if one has but a small quantity to distill, heating may be done with a burner. In this way a small amount of material can be distilled in a relatively short time.

After distillation, the diethyl adipate is poured into a bottle of suitable size. A label on which the following information is neatly printed is affixed: structural and empirical formula; molecular weight; weight in grams and per cent yield; boiling range and pressure; name. The experiment is now complete except for the writing of a report (see Chapter 12).

Other Methods of Esterification

In addition to the Fisher–Speier method, the following methods of esterification are of interest: (1) reaction of an acyl chloride with an alcohol in the presence of a base; (2) reaction of an acid with diazomethane [7]; (3) the concentrated sulfuric acid method [8]; and (4) the alkyl chlorosulfite method [9].

1. Reaction of Acyl Chloride with Alcohols

A. PREPARATION OF ACYL CHLORIDES

In order to obtain high overall yields in the conversion of an acid to an ester by this route, the acyl chloride must be prepared in high yield. The reagent most commonly used for this purpose is thionyl chloride.

$$RCOOH + SOCl_2 \rightarrow RCOCl + SO_2 + HCl$$

Because the boiling point of thionyl chloride is 75–76°C, the removal of excess reagent from the acyl chloride is easily accomplished if the acyl chloride has a sufficiently high boiling point. However, there are two side reactions which may cause the yield of acyl chloride to fall. These side reactions are anhydride formation and ketene formation.

Anhydride formation may result from: (a) reaction of an acyl chlorosulfite with another molecule of acid to form an intermediate which decomposes to yield anhydride; of (b) decomposition of the acyl chlorosulfite to yield a ketene which reacts with acid to form the anhydride.

(a)
$$RCOOH + SOCl_2 \rightarrow R\overset{\displaystyle O}{\overset{\displaystyle \|}{C}}{-}O{-}\overset{\displaystyle Cl}{\overset{\displaystyle |}{S}} \rightarrow O + HCl$$

$$R{-}\overset{\displaystyle O}{\overset{\displaystyle \|}{C}}{-}O{-}\overset{\displaystyle Cl}{\overset{\displaystyle |}{S}} \rightarrow O + RCOOH \rightarrow (RCO)_2O + SO_2 + HCl$$

(b)
$$\begin{matrix} R \\ \diagdown \\ & CHCOOH + SOCl_2 \rightarrow \\ \diagup \\ R \end{matrix}$$

$$\begin{matrix} R \\ \diagdown \\ & C{=}C{=}O \\ \diagup \\ R \end{matrix}$$

$$\begin{matrix} R \\ \diagdown \\ & C{=}C{=}O{-} \\ \diagup \\ R \end{matrix} \begin{cases} \xrightarrow{R_2CHCOOH} \text{anhydride} \\ \\ \xrightarrow{HCl} R_2CHCOCl \end{cases}$$

The complications above outlined can largely be avoided by adding a solution of the acid in methylene chloride or other inert solvent slowly to the thionyl chloride, since both routes to the anhydride require the acid to be in excess [10].

However, even when thionyl chloride is in excess, ketene formation, probably by the cyclic mechanism indicated above, can take place [11, 12]. Dimerization of a ketene intermediate may also be responsible for the formation of high-boiling residues often observed when acyl chlorides are prepared.

The other reagent commonly used for preparation of acyl chlorides is phosphorus pentachloride which reacts according to the following equation.

$$RCOOH + PCl_5 \rightarrow RCOCl + POCl_3 + HCl$$

Because of the unpleasant smell of phosphorus pentachloride, it is convenient to weigh (in a hood) a quantity of phosphorus pentachloride directly into the Claisen flask to be used for distillation of the resulting acyl chloride.

If the acyl chloride is not to be distilled, a round-bottomed flask is appropriate.

The stoichiometric amount of acid is then added to the phosphorus pentachloride, with or without added solvent. The reaction mixture usually becomes homogeneous even without solvent, as the phosphorus oxychloride formed is a good solvent for the acyl chloride. By applying suction the phosphorus oxychloride, bp 105°C, can be distilled at moderate temperatures after the reaction is complete.

Since phosphorus oxychloride has an evil, persistent smell, do not use a water pump if the effluent water will pass down a trough in the laboratory. Rather, collect the phosphorus oxychloride in a suitable cooled trap and discard it in a can made available for the disposal of noisesome or toxic solvents or reagents. It is advisable not to use a good vacuum pump for removing phosphorus oxychloride, or other corrosive chemicals, because the useful life of a pump used for such a purpose will be greatly decreased.

Although it is easier to use thionyl chloride, the higher yields of acyl chloride often obtained with phosphorus pentachloride make the latter the preferred reagent (see page 143).

B. REACTION OF ACYL CHLORIDES WITH ALCOHOLS

When an acyl chloride is reacted with an alcohol, at least one equivalent of a tertiary amine (pyridine is most commonly used) is recommended to neutralize the hydrogen chloride formed. However, urea may be used instead of the tertiary amine. Urea is amazingly efficient and, further, it is desirable because of its ease of removal during workup, lack of odor, and low price [13]. The solvents used and conditions for reaction depend upon the properties of the reactants. A common procedure involves adding a solution of the acyl chloride to a solution of the alcohol and base held at room temperature or below by means of a cooling bath. The time required is determined by the nature of the reactants as is the procedure used in isolation and purification of the products.

2. Reaction of an Acid with Diazomethane

The most rapid and quantitative method for preparing a methyl ester is to treat a solution of diazomethane in ether with the acid in question. *This is also the most dangerous because diazomethane is toxic and explosive.* If the precautions described below are followed, however, diazomethane can be prepared and handled safely. The most important thing to realize is that mixtures of diazomethane and air can be detonated by as simple an operation as putting one ground glass joint into another. For this reason, the use of cork or neoprene stoppers is recommended, and any apparatus which has a small crack or chipped lip should *not* be used.

Solutions of diazomethane can be prepared with or without distillation. The diazomethane precursors in common use are nitroso derivatives of methylamine [14]. All of these precursors should be regarded as potential skin irritants and appropriate care should be taken to avoid contact. Many workers prefer to use rubber gloves when handling potentially irritating chemicals.

Excellent directions for preparation of diazomethane by distillation are available [15]. If a solution if diazomethane in ether is desired, the distillation step may be omitted. However, when the distillation step is omitted, there are impurities in the ether solution. These impurities may necessitate additional purification of the methyl ester produced if the ester is to be submitted for elemental analyses.

The safety precautions mentioned in reference [15] should always be followed, even by experienced workers. Familiarity breeds contempt!

Safety precautions involve the use of a plastic shield, heavy gloves, and safety goggles.

If a solution of diazomethane prepared without distillation is desired, the reaction of the nitroso precursor is effected essentially as described in reference [15] except that the reaction is carried out in a flask containing about 30–40% aqueous sodium hydroxide and ether. After the reaction has been completed, the ether layer is decanted and used immediately or dried further over potassium hydroxide pellets in the refrigerator.

3. The Concentrated Sulfuric Acid (Newman) Method

About 1 g of the acid to be esterified is dissolved in 8–10 ml of 100% sulfuric acid at room temperature. This solution is then poured into an excess of the desired alcohol. After making the resulting solution basic with sodium carbonate, the mixture is worked up by an appropriate method to yield the desired ester.

This method works only for certain sterically hindered acids but has the advantage that the esters can be made rapidly in high yield. The requirement for success of this method is that an acylium ion be formed when the acid is dissolved in sulfuric acid, as indicated in the equation below.

$$RCOOH + 2H_2SO_4 \rightarrow R\overset{+}{C}O + H_3O^+ + 2HSO_4^-$$

When such a solution is poured into an alcohol, such as methanol, ethanol, or isopropyl alcohol, the corresponding ester is produced instantaneously.

$$R\overset{+}{C}O + R'OH \rightarrow RCOOR' + H^+$$

For a discussion of the reasons for the success of this procedure see the original article [8].

4. The Alkyl Chlorosulfite (Newman and Fones) Method [9]

Primary alkyl chlorosulfites are prepared by adding a primary alcohol to an excess of pure thionyl chloride at 0°C and allowing the reaction mixture to stand at room temperature for 3 days. On vacuum distillation the alkyl chlorosulfite is obtained in over 90% yield [16]. When an alkyl chlorosulfite is added to the dry sodium salt of an acid, with or without benzene as diluent, an exothermic reaction occurs. After this initial reaction has been completed the mixture is heated at 100–150°C until the evolution of sulfur dioxide is completed (1–2 hr). The ester is then isolated and purified by appropriate means. The equations involved are as follows.

$$ROH + SOCl_2 \rightarrow ROSOCl + HCl$$

$$ROSOCl + R'COONa \rightarrow R'COOSOOR$$

$$R'COOSOOR \xrightarrow{\Delta} R'COOR + SO_2$$

REFERENCES

[1] For a discussion of the various mechanisms by which acids are esterified see Hine, J., *Physical Organic Chemistry*, McGraw-Hill Book Co., Inc., New York, 1962, chap. 12 and references therein.

[2] For a discussion of steric effects in esterification see Newman, M. S. (ed.), *Steric Effects in Organic Chemistry*, John Wiley and Sons, Inc., New York, 1956, Chap. 4.

[3] Hammett, L. P., *Physical Organic Chemistry*, McGraw-Hill Book Co., Inc., New York, 1940, p. 213.

[4] See Fieser, L. F., and M. Fieser, *Reagents for Organic Synthesis*, John Wiley and Sons, Inc., New York, 1967, pp. 512–518 for many references to the use of insoluble resins as catalysts. Suitable resins may be obtained from Dow and Rohm and Haas companies.

[5] Dean, E. W., and D. D. Stark, *Ind. Eng. Chem.*, **12**, 486 (1920). The design shown in fig. 1 is more flexible because the amount of lower layer which can be accommodated is larger since a stopcock is available for withdrawal of the lower layer.

[6] Newman, M. S., *Ind. Eng. Chem.*, **12**, 274 (1940).

[7] von Pechmann, H., *Ber.*, **27**, 1888 (1894); **28**, 855 (1895).

[8] Newman, M. S., *J. Amer. Chem. Soc.*, **63**, 2431 (1941).

[9] Newman, M. S., and W. S. Fones, *J. Amer. Chem. Soc.*, **69**, 1046 (1947).

[10] See Fieser, L. F., and M. Fieser, *Reagents for Organic Synthesis*, John Wiley and Sons, Inc., New York, 1967, pp. 1158, 1159, for additional information regarding acyl chloride formation.

[11] Newman, M. S., A. Arkell, and T. Fukunaga, *J. Amer. Chem. Soc.*, **82**, 2498 (1960).

[12] Partial (or total) racemization during the formation of acyl chlorides from optically active acids occurs readily when the asymmetric center is at the α-carbon. No study of this behavior, other than that described in the M.S. thesis of Thomas Sutliff, Ohio State University, 1966, appears to have been made.

[13] Newman, M. S., and L. K. Lala, *Tetrahedron Lett.*, 3267 (1967). See also C. Bodenca, R. K. Allison, and P. H. Dirstine, *Ind. Eng. Chem.*, **43**, 1196 (1951), and W. S. Trahanovsky, M. P. Doyle, and P. D. Bartlett, *J. Org. Chem.*, **32**, 150 (1967).

[14] Fieser, L. F., and M. Fieser, *Reagents for Organic Synthesis*, John Wiley and Sons, Inc., New York, 1967, pp. 191–192.

[15] Moore, J. A., and D. E. Reed, *Organic Syntheses*, vol. **41**, 1961, p. 16. References to a number of other organic syntheses preparations of diazomethane are given.

[16] Carre, P., and D. Libermann, *Bull. Soc. Chim.*, [4] **53**, 1002 (1933).

Two

Purification of
Pyrene

The objective of this experiment is to provide experience in the purification of small amounts of solid aromatic polycyclic hydrocarbons (or derivatives thereof).

The techniques discussed are π-complex formation, fractional crystallization, chromatography, melting-point determination, vacuum sublimation, and thin-layer chromatography.

Small amounts of solids frequently need purification. The following discussion is limited to procedures pertinent to the purification of compounds which have at least two fused aromatic rings. None the less, many of the principles involved are generally applicable to other compounds. The compound chosen for this experiment is crude commercial pyrene, and the student is required to hand in a minimum of 300 mg of pure pyrene from a 500-mg sample (smaller-scale experiments may be chosen if desired). In all of the operations discussed, quantitative transfers must be effected as described before (see page 12).

The pyrene sample we have used was obtained from the Union Carbide Corporation (RD-383-43).

If more than one technique is to be used in purifying a solid, the order in which the techniques are to be applied must be chosen. In general any method works better after another method has been applied. Hence, the order in which the following discussions are presented does not mean that the operations should always (or ever) be carried out in this order.

π-Complex Formation

Most polycyclic aromatic compounds form reasonably stable π-complexes with a variety of reagents [1, 2]. Picric acid has probably been used more frequently than any other electron-acceptor molecule. 2,4,7-Trinitrofluorenone [3, 4] and 2,4,5,7-tetranitro-fluorenone [5] are also recommended.

The use of picric acid is particularly recommended whenever the purification of appreciable amounts of material involve complex formation. The reasons for this preference are the following: picric acid can be so strongly absorbed on alumina that chromatographic separation is greatly simplified; and picric acid, because of its acidic hydrogen, can be extracted by washing organic solvent layers with aqueous base.

The following description of picrate formation, recrystallization, and decomposition to regenerate pyrene is general. When picric acid and pyrene are dissolved in a solvent, the following equilibria are of interest.

pyrene

picric acid

$$\text{Pyrene} + \text{picric acid} \rightleftharpoons \begin{bmatrix} \text{pyrene–picric} \\ \text{acid complex,} \\ \text{soluble} \end{bmatrix} \rightleftharpoons \begin{bmatrix} \text{pyrene–picric} \\ \text{acid complex,} \\ \text{insoluble} \end{bmatrix}$$

Pure pyrene and picric acid are colorless.

Picric acid as usually obtained is yellow due to the presence of small amounts of picrate anion.

To obtain the solid red complex, the pyrene and a small excess of picric acid should be dissolved in a suitable solvent in a small E flask and heated until a clear solution results.

Erlenmeyer flasks are preferred to beakers for all crystallizations for the following reasons;

1. *Quantitative transfer from an E flask is relatively easy but difficult from a beaker because rinsing the outside of a beaker is tedious, time consuming, and wasteful of solvent. The larger the beaker the more tedious.*
2. *Evaporation from a beaker is not easily prevented, whereas an E flask is easily stoppered. If evaporation occurs in a beaker, solids which are not in equilibrium with the solvent and solute separate on the sides of the beaker above the solution. This feature defeats the purpose of a crystallization.*
3. *Often it is desirable to distil solvent from a filtrate or solution. This is more conveniently done using a flask and the apparatus shown in Figure 1–5, page 20, than by distilling from an open beaker (danger, odor).*

A solvent mixture that is recommended for picrate formation and purification is benzene-ethanol. The hydrocarbons are usually more soluble in benzene and less soluble in alcohol, whereas picric acid is more soluble in alcohol than in benzene. With some experience the best proportions of each for the crystallization of picrates of different aromatic substrates can readily be found. During concentration of solutions a solvent richer in either benzene or alcohol can be produced as desired by taking advantage of the distillation behavior of solutions of benzene–alcohol (see page 11). With a little experience the color while hot can be used to indicate whether the volume of solution is such that a proper amount of picrate will separate on standing at room temperature. The reasons for operating at room temperature rather than in the cold are discussed later under Fractional Crystallization (see page 55). If concentration is carried

Most solid picrates are of the 1:1 type, but other ratios may be involved.

too far, picrates of other components may contaminate the pyrene picrate.

These complexes are called picrates; this is a misnomer as picrates should refer only to salts of picric acid (compounds which contain the picrate anion) whereas the complexes are of the donor-acceptor type. Such picrate complexes should be stored only in Pyrex containers because the alkali in soft glasses causes a yellow nontransparent haze to coat soft glass in time.

The pyrene picrate which has crystallized is now collected by suction filtration in a small funnel. In Figure 2-1 two types useful for the collection of small quantities of solids are shown; (a) a Buchner type funnel with fritted glass disc (various porosities are available); and (b) a porcelain Hirsch funnel (also made in glass with sintered glass filters). The apparatus shown in Figure 2-2 is convenient for suction filtration. The funnel, fitted with a neoprene stopper, is put into the suction flask A held firmly by a clamp at B. A small disc of filter paper C is placed on the filter plate D of the funnel and wet with about 1 ml of a solvent mixture similar to that in which the solid to be collected is suspended. This should be done before vacuum is applied so that the paper disc will not be sucked dry but will be held in proper position for the subsequent filtration.

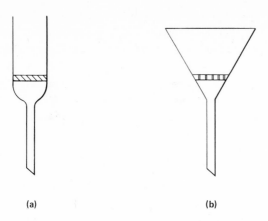

(a)   (b)

Figure 2-1. Small funnels for suction filtration. (**a**) Buchner type funnel. (**b**) Porcelain Hirsch funnel.

Small filter paper discs are available. If analytical samples are to be collected, "hardened" filter paper discs should be used as these are less likely to introduce a fibrous impurity into the sample.

When the rubber tubing E is connected to apply suction, it is preferable to have stopcock F open and stopcock H in the suction flask I about half open so that only very slight suction is applied at first. When some of the material to be filtered is poured into the funnel, stopcock H is closed, and, shortly after, stopcock F is closed. There should be a firm clamp at G so that this stopcock can be closed with one hand while the other hand, holding the flask

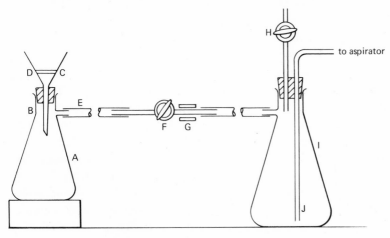

Figure 2-2. Suction filtration apparatus.

which is to be emptied into the funnel, is held in proper position over the funnel. If too much suction is applied at first, solvent may evaporate in the funnel so rapidly that solid separates in the pores of the filter paper disc (or sintered glass plate). When this happens subsequent filtration is very slow, or uneven, or both.

The closure of stopcock F after appreciable suction has been applied is important for similar reasons. If this stopcock is not closed, the additional suction applied often causes the filtrate to boil over so that material goes into the adapter and into the vacuum line. If filtration is slow, evaporation at the bottom of the filter paper disc may cause solid to crystallize due to loss of solvent. If filtration is rapid, a stream of air is sucked over the collected crystals before the adhering mother liquor is washed off. All of these sources of error are eliminated by proper manipulation of stopcocks F and H. When F is closed with a vacuum in A, all of the liquid on the funnel will be sucked through, but only enough air will enter at the end of the filtration to fill the flask. If filtration slows, more suction may easily be applied by proper manipulation of F. This procedure permits working at a proper pace. After transferring quantitatively all of the solid and mother liquor with the aid of picric acid–saturated solvent (to prevent dissociation of the picrate which might occur if pure solvent were used) and rinsing the mother liquor off of the crystals, sucking air over the crystals is proper since only traces of picric acid (in the adhering wash liquor) will be precipitated on the solid.

In general the technique of collection of solids by suction filtration is not properly carried out. Too often air is sucked over the solid before the adhering mother liquor is washed off.

The picrate thus obtained may be recrystallized by redissolving in benzene-alcohol and collecting again by suction filtration. The picrate may now be decomposed to yield the purified pyrene. For the decomposition of small amounts (0.5–5.0 g) of picrate, column chromatography, as described in the following section is recommended. When large amounts of picrates are involved, extraction of the picric acid into a basic solution may be preferable to large-scale chromatography. In such cases aqueous solutions of diethanolamine are preferable to sodium or potassium hydroxide solutions because of the limited water solubility of sodium and potassium picrates. Pyrene may be isolated from the eluate by chromatography or from an ether-benzene solution if the alkaline extraction method is used.

In general, whenever the alkali salts of organic acids are of limited water solubility, the solubility of diethanolamine salts should be tested.

Chromatography

There are many different ways in which solids (also liquids and gases) may be purified by the technique of chromatography.

A small column is prepared by filling the column A, Figure 2-3, with activated alumina to a height B determined by the amount of picrate to be decomposed. There are several grades of activated alumina that may be used. For much chromatography standardized grades of Woelm alumina are recommended, and their use is described in many of the books on chromatography. For chromatography of picrates, Alcoa grade F-20 alumina is sufficient. The alumina is activated by heating in an E flask held at 160–170° in a fused salt bath (see page 24) until the evolution of adsorbed moisture is completed (about 1–2 hr). When the alumina is prepared in this manner picric acid does not move down, even on lengthy elution with benzene. Thus a column of 1–2 in. of alumina is ample to decompose as much as 2 g of picrate. A small amount of cotton or glass wool should be placed at C and the column partly filled with solvent (in this case benzene).

For best results distilled benzene or other solvent should be used to ensure the absence of a nonvolatile residue.

The alumina should be added slowly to the column in such a way that it is evenly distributed. Before adding the picrate solution to this column, the solvent should be allowed to drain off through stopcock D until the level is about 1/2 in. above B. As concentrated a solution of the picrate as convenient should be added to the column (using quantitative transfer technique) while D is closed. D is then opened and elution started, more benzene being added to the column as necessary to keep the top of the column B covered with at least 1/2 in. of solvent. The rate of elution is conveniently regulated by D. If desirable, the height E of liquid in the column may be kept constant by supporting a separatory funnel F as shown with the stopcock G left open and the plug H in place. Air can only enter F through the

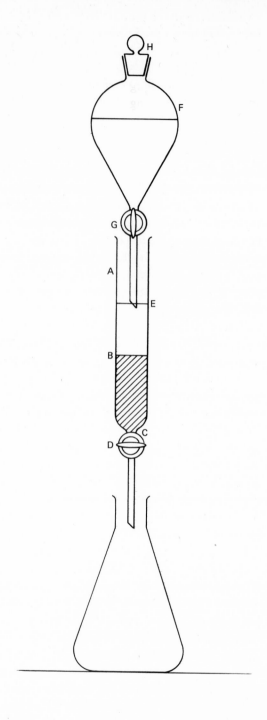

Figure 2-3. Column for elution chromatography.

An Advanced Organic Laboratory Course

tip of the separatory funnel; hence, the height is controlled at E as long as there is liquid in F. By controlling the rate of elution at stopcock D, the rate of elution may be slowed so that more time will be required. However, the working time may be less as other things can be done while elution is taking place.

In the case of pyrene picrate decomposition the progress of the chromatography is easy to follow: the picric acid forms a yellow layer at the top of B; the pyrene solution is characterized by an intense blue-violet fluorescence if viewed in ultraviolet light.

An ultraviolet hand lamp is useful for many purposes in the laboratory and should be available. For example, when working with materials which fluoresce in ultraviolet light, examination of the skin on hands and arms allows you to know when all such material has been removed by proper cleansing. This safety feature is strongly recommended. A A variety of ultraviolet lamps is described in apparatus catalogs. **Overexposure to ultraviolet light should be avoided.**

After the pyrene has been eluted, the benzene is distilled to a small volume and the purification of pyrene, as far as picrate formation is concerned, is complete.

The chromatography of pyrene picrate is so easily effected that elaborate precautions for producing a uniformly packed alumina column are unnecessary. However, when more difficult separations are involved, even packing of the absorbent is necessary. The device illustrated in Figure 2-4 is recommended.

Dry absorbent A is placed in the chromatographic column B provided with a coarse fritted disk C to support the adsorbent. The lower end of the column is attached by a Tygon fitting D to a T-tube E which, in turn, is connected by a Tygon fitting to a submersible pump F and to a Tygon tube G fitted with a screw clamp H.

A Little Giant submersible pump, Model 1, obtained from the Little Giant Co., Oklahoma City, Oklahoma, is satisfactory.

The upper end of the column is fitted with a neoprene stopper which contains a U-tube I connected to a drying tube J filled with glass wool K. To pack the column, a solvent, for example, hexane or benzene, is poured in to wet the adsorbent and to fill the container L, a large crystallizing dish, to a height M. This provides enough solvent to fill the column to N, the lower end of the U-tube. The

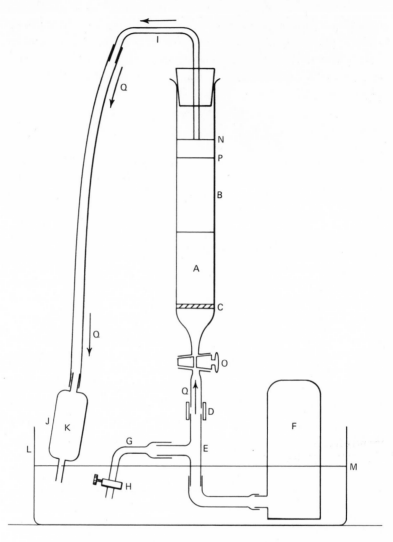

Figure 2-4. Packing of chromatographic column.

pump is started with the stopcock O closed and the screw clamp H partly open. The stopcock is then opened slowly so that any air bubbles expelled upward by the pump F do not cause too much turbulence in the column. With a little practice, the degree of opening of the stopcock O and the screw clamp H can be regulated so that the suspension of adsorbent will level off just below N—for instance at a point P about 1/2 to 1 in. below N. The solvent which circulates through the system in the direction shown by the arrows Q soon (5–10 min) creates a mobile system which distributes the absorbent uniformly in the liquid phase. As solvent circulates, it is filtered from suspended adsorbent by the glass wool K in tube J. To stop the process, merely shut stopcock O, turn off the pump, and disconnect the chromatographic column which is ready for use as soon as the absorbent settles [6].

Fractional Crystallization [7]

Perhaps the most widely used method of purification of solids is fractional crystallization. The procedure is simple. A solid is dissolved by heating in a suitable solvent. On cooling, part of the solid separates as crystals and part remains in the mother liquor. The fraction which crystallizes is separated from the mother liquor and is purer than the original solid. This process is repeated as often as required, until solid of sufficient purity for the purpose at hand is obtained. In the following discussion the variables to be considered are solvent, temperature control, method of separation of solid and mother liquid, use of decolorizing charcoal, and estimation of purity.

1. Solvent

In most laboratory manuals single solvent use is recommended. The term single solvent means that only one solvent is used for dissolving the solid by heating, for filtration by gravity to remove insoluble impurities, and for allowing the final equilibrium between crystals and mother liquor to be established. Much time is wasted in trying to do single-solvent recrystallization, especially in the filtration part. Too often, the hot solution cools during filtration by gravity through a filter paper folded into a funnel; crystallization then soon clogs the filter paper and funnel so that time (and often compound) is lost.

Vacuum filtration is generally not recommended because the rapid cooling of the first portion to come in contact with the funnel causes blockage.

Recrystallization involving two solvents should be used whenever possible; one solvent which is a very good solvent for the compound in question and one solvent which is poor.

To ascertain solubilities, put a small amount of solid in a small test tube and add a few drops of solvent. Do not shake—leave as still as

convenient. The behavior of the solid should then be observed im-
mediately with a low-power hand lens. In particular, observe the rate
of solution by noting the diffusion rings (similar to currents of hot air
rising from a road in summer) in the solvent. In the case of higher
molecular weight compounds, do not decide too quickly that a sub-
stance is insoluble in a solvent, because the rate *of solution may be slow.*
Thin-layer chromatography may also be useful in selection of solvent
(see page 69).

The good solvent is necessary because crude solids often have to be transferred quantitatively from the funnel in which they have been collected by filtration. Also, such solids must often be filtered to remove insoluble substances, dirt, and so on. Both of these operations can be carried out rapidly if a good solvent is used. After the transfer or filtration is complete, the solution should be concentrated to a proper volume and diluted with the poor solvent. Crystallization will then proceed. Naturally, experience is needed to tell just how much of each type of solvent is best for the crystallization at hand.

Care must be taken not to add too much of the poor solvent at first because too much (and hence less pure) material may crystallize in the first crop. If too little of the poor solvent is used, the mis-calculation is easy to correct by adding more; however, if too much is used the mistake takes more time to rectify. Furthermore, if too much of the poor solvent is added, the formation of two immiscible layers may occur when low-melting materials are involved.

One of the most useful mixed solvent systems is benzene–alcohol. Benzene is a good nonpolar solvent and alcohol a good polar solvent. The two are miscible in all proportions and form a minimum boiling azeotrope (see page 11) so that, by distillation, one can approach a benzene-rich or an alcohol-rich solvent mixture as needed for the crystallization at hand. Furthermore, distillation of a benzene-alcohol solution of a substance insures that all water present is removed because of the minimum boiling ternary azeotrope situation (see page 10). In the case of pyrene, benzene is a good solvent and alcohol a poor one so that by proper choice of a mixture excellent recrystallizations may be effected.

When a compound is to be purified by recrystallization, the solubility should be tested in a variety of solvents so that choice of a good and a poor solvent can be made. The combination of solvents chosen preferably will include liquids which have nearly the same boiling point so that the composition will not change very much

when concentration of the mother liquor by distillation takes ↓
If a saturated hydrocarbon is indicated as the poor solvent,
petroleum fractions having about the same boiling point as that
a good solvent. For example, cyclohexane (bp 81°C) is excellent
use with benzene (bp 78°C).

2. Temperature Control

After obtaining a hot solution of the material to be crystallized
in a suitable solvent, the next step is to decide how rapidly the solution should be cooled and whether the final equilibrium should be
established at room temperature or lower. Obviously there cannot
be one answer for the many situations which arise in practice, but
the following discussion will serve to point out some of the factors
involved in making a choice.

Crystallization at room temperature is preferable to that in the
cold because it is easier to separate the crystals from the mother
liquor without disturbing the equilibrium. If cold suspensions are
to be filtered, one must work rapidly and use precooled funnels
(when small volumes are involved). Also the solvent used to wash
adhering mother liquor from the crystals must be precooled. If there
is any appreciable humidity, the condensation of moisture may also
be annoying and detrimental. If the rate of filtration is slow for any
reason, the temperature rises and more solid is dissolved in the
mother liquor. By proper manipulation of two solvents you can
almost always find the proper proportions so that crystallization at
room temperature is satisfactory.

The rate of cooling is an important factor in controlling the
average size of crystals formed. In general rapid cooling causes the
formation of small crystals whereas slow cooling yields larger
crystals. If large crystals are desired (see below) crystal nuclei must
be provided while the solution is still warm so that supersaturation
does not occur to any large extent.

*Supersaturation can occur to such a large extent that, when seed
crystals are added to the solution at room temperature, crystallization
occurs so rapidly that the solvent is brought to boiling.*

It is not satisfactory to nucleate by adding a few crystals to the body
of a hot solution in which the rate of cooling is to be slow because
the seeds may dissolve. A better procedure is to place a few small
crystals on the tip of a stirring rod moistened with solution and rub

these on the walls of the E flask well above the level of the solution. The flask is then stoppered and placed in a large beaker fitted on the bottom and sides with cotton for insulation so that the rate of cooling will be slow. This flask should then rest *undisturbed* until equilibrium has been established. This may take anywhere from an hour to a few days. The rate of crystallization of higher molecular weight compounds is often slower than that of lower molecular weight compounds. Although it takes more time to cool a solution slowly, cooling time is not working time; other operations can be carried out while waiting for a slow crystallization to be effected. In addition, considerable working time may be gained in the separation of crystals and mother liquor (see the following discussion).

Another advantage is occasionally gained by slow crystallization. If a mixture of compounds A and B, is at hand, their separation by fractional crystallization is often tedious. If large crystals are formed by slow crystallization from the proper solvent, it is often possible to separate some crystals of A and B by hand sorting and then apply what may be called *kinetic crystallization*. Separation of components A and B is accomplished by taking advantage of different rates of crystallization rather than different solubilities, as follows.

Separate small amounts of A and B by hand (the use of a low power magnifying glass and a thin spatula is recommended). Then recrystallize these samples of A and B separately several times until samples of pure A and pure B are at hand. Prepare a slightly supersaturated solution of the mixture of A and B and seed with powdered A. The powdered material is used in order to get a large number of seeds. Since the rate of crystallization of A is large because of the many seeds of pure A present, the mixture should be filtered after a short time to yield an appreciable amount of almost pure A. The material in the mother liquor can be processed similarly (in the same or a different solvent), using pure B to seed. This process of kinetic crystallization is only of value if reasonably large amounts of material are involved. If small amounts of products have to be separated, some kind of chromatography is usually preferable.

Another reason for preferring slow cooling and the formation of large crystals is that large crystals are easier to collect (see the discussion which follows) and bottle. Small crystals often develop static charges on drying which make their transfer difficult and wasteful. Furthermore, the often-stated warning that large crystals are more likely to contain occluded impurities is invalid. If solvent of crystallization is present in the crystals, the solvent molecules are pure and do not contain solute. When solvent of crystallization is removed from the crystals (usually clear when solvated and opaque when solvent-free), there is no occluded impurity due to the solvent. Actually small crystals are more likely to entrap solvent containing solute as they grow rapidly and may form an overall structure which entraps solution. Clathyrate formation [8] is a different phenomenon. In addition, since small crystals present a larger surface area than do large crystals, adsorption of impurities may lead to a less pure solid.

3. Method of Separation of Solid and Mother Liquid

The method most often recommended for collection of the solid is suction filtration using apparatus similar to that shown in Figures 2-1 and 2-2. The objective in such filtrations is to separate the solid crystals from the mother liquor as well as possible. There are two main reasons for inefficient crystallization: adherence of the mother liquor to the solid, and the solution of crystals during attempts to remove the adhering mother liquor by washing with solvent. Avoid sucking much air through the solid on the funnel so that the solvent in the mother liquor adhering to the solid is not evaporated (see the precautions mentioned earlier, page 48, in connection with collection of pyrene picrate). Should evaporation occur, the crystals would be coated with less pure material which was present in the mother liquor. Even though the amount of impurity thus introduced is small, the appearance of the crystals suffers. One should always try to obtain not only the purest but also the best-looking crystals. Showmanship is a part of superior laboratory technique!

After the crystals have been collected on the funnel and the filtrate is in the receiver, it is necessary to rinse down the crystallization flask, including the outside of the neck, the funnel, and the crystals with fresh solvent. The composition of the solvent should be adjusted so that the wash solution is somewhat richer in the poor solvent than the solvent mixture in which the crystallization took place. If the solid is to be recrystallized, all of the crystals need not be removed from the crystallization flask because the crystals on the funnel are to be returned to this flask for further purification. If the solid collected represents the final pure product, as much as possible should be collected on the funnel.

In moderate to large-scale vacuum filtrations, the use of a rubber dam is often helpful in effecting a better separation of crystals and mother liquor. This technique is applied as shown in Figure 2-5. After most of the mother liquor has been sucked into the filter flask, a flexible piece of rubber A is placed over the Buchner funnel B and tied on at C (stout rubber bands are useful). When further suction is applied at D, the air forces the rubber dam to press down on the crystals E and thus more mother liquor is expressed. In addition, the top can be pressed with the fingers. This procedure is best applied after the original mother liquor has been washed through with wash solvent as described above.

When rubber dams are used they should be cleaned immediately after use. If left encrusted with compounds the rubber soon looses its elasticity and splits when used again. The rubber dam technique is not recommended when low-boiling solvents are used because of ebullition of the solvent under reduced pressure and evaporation of solvent from mother liquor adhering to the crystals.

If several recrystallizations of a mixture must be carried out, much time is expended in collecting the crystals, washing them free of mother liquor, and returning them to a flask for recrystallization. A procedure which cuts down markedly on the time involved is recommended. It is worth spending some time to find a solvent

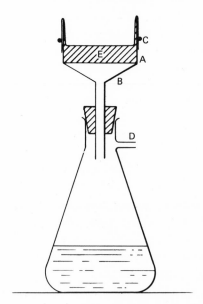

Figure 2-5. Use of a rubber dam in vacuum filtration.

system in which the crystals that separate are firmly attached to the bottom and sides of the flask. A slow crystallization technique is usually necessary to attain this objective, as large crystals are preferable. When the crystals adhere to the flask merely pour off the mother liquor slowly into another flask and rinse the crystals with a suitable solvent mixture. Thus the crystals are all in the original flask and the mother liquor in the other flask. This process can be repeated the desired number of times and all the vacuum filtration steps except the last may be entirely avoided.

In working with small amounts of solid, it is often desirable to do the recrystallizations in a test tube. The mother liquor can be removed from the crystals with a pipette.

To get a second crop in all recrystallization schemes, the mother liquor must be concentrated to a volume smaller than that from which the first crop of crystals was obtained. The techniques involved are similar and need not be stressed. In any particular purification the optimum number of recrystallizations of the main and secondary crops must be worked out with the ultimate use of the compound in mind. If the ultimate use involves a further chemical reaction, an entire crude crop of crystals may be used without any purification. To find out how much purification is needed measure two overall yields: one in which the entire crude product is processed and the final product purified; and the other in which the crude product is purified, the purified product then processed, and the final product again purified. Whether LM is equal to, greater than, or less than NPQ must be determined in each case. These schemes are

$$\text{crude A} \xrightarrow{L\%} \text{crude B} \searrow^{M\%}$$
$$\Big\downarrow N\% \qquad\qquad\qquad\qquad \nearrow \text{pure B}$$
$$\text{pure A} \xrightarrow{P\%} \text{crude B} \nearrow^{Q\%}$$

Finally, the physical chemistry of purification by crystallization includes many complicating patterns. The student is advised to review periodically the types of situations which may be met [9].

4. The Use of Decolorizing Charcoal

The use of charcoal is often recommended to remove small amounts of colored impurities. Often this procedure is helpful;

however, before it is applied its effectiveness should be tried on a small scale in a small test tube. If a colored solution of the compound is treated with a small amount of charcoal and the tube viewed carefully, it is often possible to determine whether the colored impurity is being absorbed or not. If the procedure is effective, the charcoal treatment should be carried out at room temperature rather than at reflux (as often recommended). The decolorization depends on preferential absorption, and the ratios for absorption are generally greater at lower, rather than at higher, temperatures. Also, too much charcoal should not be used because a certain amount of the desired compound may also be absorbed and lost.

Darco G-60 is generally a very good decolorizing carbon. Norite-A is also available and may be preferable in certain cases.

One disadvantage to the use of charcoal in the preparation of an analytical sample should be stressed. When the charcoal is removed by filtration, a small amount of colloidal charcoal always goes through the filter paper. Hence the first crop of crystals contains some charcoal and poor analyses may result. Further, the appearance is a bit off color. One recrystallization (including a filtration) is usually sufficient to remove this charcoal.

5. Estimation of Purity

As mentioned in section 3, the purity required must be determined for each case if the material is to be used in a subsequent reaction. In general if the material is to undergo catalytic hydrogenation over a heterogeneous catalyst, the rate of hydrogenation will be greater the greater the purity of the sample (and of the solvent used in the hydrogenation).

If the material is intended for biological evaluation or involvement in a free radical chain reaction, extreme purity is highly desirable. In order to estimate purity to this degree the ordinary criteria, such as melting point and spectral analyses (infrared, ultraviolet, and nuclear magnetic resonance) are often inadequate. Mass spectral analysis and thin-layer chromatography (see page 66) may be useful in many cases. When compounds are being purified for elemental analyses, a careful filtration should be carried out during the last recrystallization. The solvent for washing and collecting the solid should be freshly filtered before use. All funnels and flasks to be used for processing a sample intended for analysis should be washed clean of any dirt or lint particles with **filtered** solvent. Hardened filter paper should be used if Buchner funnels are used. Air should not be sucked over the crystals for much time because dust or lint may be sucked onto the sample.

When I was visiting at the University of Glasgow in 1957, it was common knowledge that the chief analyst would refuse to analyze any sample in which he could detect a speck of dirt with a hand lens.

If any material requires recrystallization for any of the above reasons, do not waste time by doing only one recrystallization. Recrystallize at least twice before trying to determine purity again.

Traditionally, the melting point of compounds has been used to estimate purity. The phrase "recrystallize to constant melting point" means that a substance is recrystallized until the melting point is constant for the last two determinations. If this criterion is used, the last crystallization should take place in a solvent as much different in type from the previously used solvent as allowed by the nature of the substance. The reason for this is that sometimes two compounds crystallize together in one solvent system and, thus, behave as though a single compound were present.

The melting point as a criterion of purity does not have the same priority now as it did relatively few years ago. The use of thin-plate chromatography, nuclear magnetic resonance, and mass spectral analysis often provides more sensitive probes of purity. However, the careful determination of melting point is still very useful and worthy of detailed comment.

An excellent way of determining the melting point of typical organic compounds is by using a Hershberg melting-point apparatus[10] (see Figure 2-6). This apparatus may be heated electrically or by a flame. For accurate melting-point determination stem corrections must be made and United States Bureau of Standards calibrated short-stem thermometers must be used.

It is advisable to check any thermometer used at 0 (ice point) and at 100°C (boiling point of water) to see that the temperature scale is approximately correct because occasionally thermometers that are ± 10°C are obtained.

Except in rare cases, however, the absolute melting point need not be known; rather, the melting range is of interest. Too often, the melting points reported in the literature do not truly describe the melting phenomena observed. Rather, the melting range of the last portion of solid which is observed to melt is given. These values are probably given because of a reluctance to report a melting range of several degrees for a compound upon which much time has been spent in purification. Pure compounds are assumed always to have sharp melting points but this is not always true. The technique which follows is necessary to observe the true melting range carefully; some of the complications which arise are also described.

If a relatively large amount of material is available, one can determine a melting point by measurement of the time-temperature cooling curve. Students have often done this with the ethyl hydrogen adipate obtained from the work described in Chapter 3.

About 2–3 mm of solid is placed in a Pyrex capillary tube (these can be made or bought) A which is long enough to extend from the apparatus at the top as shown.

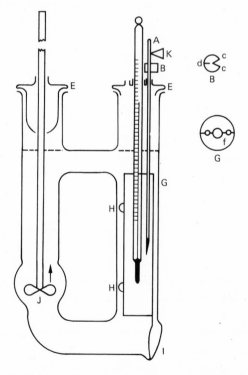

Figure 2-6. Hershberg melting-point apparatus.

The solids may be packed into the bottom of the tube by dropping the capillary through a length of about 1/4-in. inside diameter (ID) tubing held upright over an inverted crystallizing dish. The bouncing of the capillary tube on the crystallizing dish causes solids to accumulate in the bottom of the tube quite rapidly. In general the sample taken for a melting-point determination should not be packed too tightly.

These tubes may be held in place conveniently by cutting small sections of rubber stoppers B as shown. When the latter are pressed together at c the slit d opens and can be clamped on the capillary A as shown when pressure at c is released. The capillary goes through a small opening in the glass lid E and through a loop in the twisted platinum wire guide f which is fused to the top of the glass cylinder G. This cylinder G is fitted into the apparatus by the small glass bumps H (only two are shown but at each level there should be three equally spaced) and is kept from changing position when the stirrer is activated by the glass leg and pit I. Care must be taken that the leg is placed on G so that the alignment of the loops f at the top is correct.

As the temperature is raised (the stirrer J should rotate so that it propels the liquid upwards) the behavior of the solid in the capillary is observed through a magnifying glass. Rubbing a good triangular file at K causes the crystals in A to jump about. As soon as the crystals cease this free jumping some phase change is occurring. This temperature should be noted as it represents the start of melting. As the temperature is raised slowly the point when no haziness remains and a clear liquid is present can be observed. The temperature at this point represents the top of the melting range.

The melting range of 0.2°C for pure pyrene is the sharpest of any organic compound I have ever observed.

The melting behavior described above is that of a pure compound which is not solvated, is thermally stable, and does not have polymorphic forms. Not many compounds meet these criteria. Polymorphic forms are much more prevalent than is appreciated. A typical melting-point behavior for a compound which has polymorphic forms is as follows.

On slow heating the crystals will cease to jump around on filing at K at some temperature, for example, 130°C. However, the still-solid material shows no sign of melting at 132°. If a thin wire is inserted into the capillary A to break up the solid, renewed filing at K shows that the crystals now jump around again. As further heat is applied the crystals may stop bouncing at 134° and be completely melted at 135°. When subjected to the technique described, many compounds exhibit this behavior, which may be attributed to conversion of one polymorphic form to another during the slow heating process. In some cases this behavior may be due to solvent of crystallization which is removed only with difficulty.

The important feature of the Hershberg apparatus is the internal column G. When the apparatus is working properly one can move the thermometer bulb for appreciable distances up and down and side to side within G without appreciable change in the temperature reading. The flowing current of liquid which moves between the column and the wall effectively insulates the interior portion. Hence the material in the capillary tube need not be exactly adjacent to the thermometer bulb. Also, two determinations, for example, a melting point and a mixed melting point, may be taken at once with the assurance that the temperature is the same in the vicinity of each melting-point tube.

The choice of a liquid for any melting-point apparatus is con- troversial. Concentrated sulfuric acid is preferred by some for the following reasons. First, when it darkens on use (as all liquids do), it can be easily decolorized by adding a few drops of concentrated nitric acid which removes the color on heating. Second, it does not expand as much on heating as do organic liquids; hence, there is less trouble in operating the stirrer with regard to the trapping of air. The main disadvantage of sulfuric acid, the tendency to absorb water, is not serious if the melting point apparatus is used fre- quently and the glass cover E fits fairly well. Also, the used acid can readily be poured out and the apparatus washed with water and replenished with fresh acid. Sulfuric acid is not satisfactory for taking melting points much above 210°C. For such purposes a melting-point block [11] is recommended. Silicones are also often recom- mended.

A study of the behavior on melting of an organic compound which is to be sent for elemental analyses is quite useful. Close observation of the liquid melt immediately after (and often during) melting can indicate whether any solvent remains in the sample. When the crystal structure is destroyed on melting, the solvent escapes and can be observed as tiny bubbles.

Of course, loss of solvent must be distinguished from melting with decomposition.

If there is a tendency to hold solvent, the analytical sample should be melted and allowed to solidify. This solid should then be submitted for analysis without further treatment.

In my experience, the most frequent cause for poor analyses is solvent strongly held by the compound in question. Either the melting procedure described or vacuum sublimation (see the discussion which follows) is strongly recommended wherever applicable.

Vacuum Sublimation

Another procedure by which solids may be purified is vacuum sublimation. In this process a solid is heated under reduced pressure at temperatures below its melting point. Condensation of the vapor occurs on a cooled surface placed near the heated solid. A suitable apparatus is shown in Figure 2-7. Other types of sublimation apparatus are illustrated in glass company catalogs.

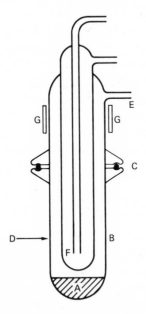

Figure 2-7. Vacuum sublimation apparatus.

The material A to be sublimed is placed in the lower part B of the apparatus which is connected to the upper half by the O-ring seal at C. The heating bath is raised until the level of heating medium is about at D and a vacuum (1 mm or less) is applied at E while cooling water is run through the internal condenser F. The apparatus is clamped *firmly* at G. The temperature is then raised until condensation on F is observed. Again, experience dictates the optimum temperature (and pressure) for each case.

After a suitable amount of material has collected on the condenser F and heating bath is removed, the vacuum released, and the lower half B is gently disengaged from the upper half. This operation can be very exasperating. If the crystals which collect are long and not well attached to F, the slightest jarring action will cause most of them to shake off. Apparatus with an O-ring seal is preferable because the separation of the two halves can be accomplished with less jarring action than when ℑ joints are involved.

If the sublimation and collection of material is to be repeated several times, it is better to rinse sublimed material off into a flask with a good solvent rather than to try to scrape it off with a spatula. In the latter case static charges often develop and make the transfer difficult.

Sublimation is recommended as a step in the purification of small amounts of material; it is not often suggested when large amounts are to be purified. However, vacuum sublimation should be applied *whenever possible* in the final stage of purification of compounds for analysis. The main reason is that sublimed samples rarely contain any solvent. The melting points of sublimed samples are often lower than those of samples before sublimation. This is due to the formation of polymorphic forms. The spectra obtained from such samples are identical with those of the pure samples. Of course, only compounds which are thermally stable at the sublimation temperature should be sublimed.

Thin Layer Chromatography (tlc) [12]

This technique is extremely useful for many purposes. The following may be mentioned: to give an estimate of the purity of a compound; to determine how many components there are in a mixture; to help in selecting solvents for recrystallization and/or column chromatography; to obtain information about how to conduct a reaction; and to isolate small amounts of pure components from a mixture rapidly. Before discussing these uses comments concerning thin layer chromatography are in order.

If a thin glass plate A containing a layer of adsorbent B is placed in a vessel C which contains a pool of solvent D (as shown in Figure 2-8), the solvent rises uniformly in the adsorbent B if the latter has been evenly applied to the plate A. Lid E should be placed over the top so that solvent movement practically ceases when the solvent front reaches the top of the plate. If a small amount of a compound is placed on the adsorbent at a spot F at the bottom of a plate before putting the plate in the solvent, the compound moves upward on the plate at a rate which is characteristic of the compound, the adsorbent, and the solvent.

The rate of movement of a compound on a given adsorbent using a given solvent is expressed as the R_f value defined as follows:

$$R_f = \frac{distance\ of\ substance\ from\ starting\ position}{distance\ of\ solvent\ front\ from\ starting\ position}$$

If one assumes that the plate was removed (see Figure 2-8) when the solvent front reached H, the R_f value for this situation would be (distance FG)/(distance FH).

If the compound is colored, the position G can be observed. If it is colorless, its presence can be located by placing the plate in a container similar to C filled with iodine vapor. The difference in adsorption of iodine on the plate caused by the presence of G or its absence allows the position of the compound to be determined.

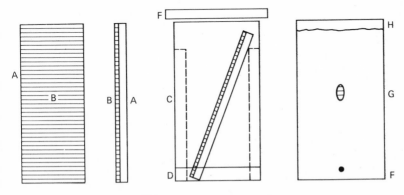

Figure 2-8. Thin-layer chromatography apparatus.

After removing the plate and heating to remove solvent, the location of the compound at G can be determined by visual methods.

For other methods which have been used to locate the positions of colorless components consult any of the texts referred to in reference [12].

1. Coating of Plates A with Absorbent B

For many purposes microscope slides make convenient plates. As shown in Figure 2-9, slurry A of the adsorbent (40 g, Silica-Gel G, Merck–Darmstadt) in 160 ml of water is placed in a spraying device B. Air from a pressure line is introduced by a tube connected at C, and the rate of spraying is easily controlled by placing a finger on the hole D. The plates (about 120–140) are placed on any smooth surface and sprayed evenly with the fine mist of silica gel slurry emanating from E. After drying at room temperature or at 100–110°C the plates are ready for use. The temperature at which drying is recommended varies for different cases.

For techniques involving larger plates and other adsorbents see reference [12].

The spraying is best done on humid days because the slower rate of drying yields fewer plates in which the adsorbent has cracked. Silica gel containing small amounts of plaster of paris as binding agent is often used.

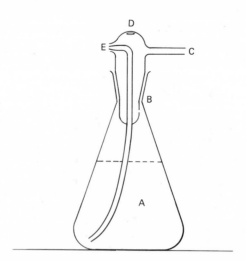

Figure 2-9. Spraying device.

2. Spotting of Plates

After the thin layer chromatography plates have been prepared, a very small amount of the substance to be chromatographed is placed at one end of the plate. This is accomplished by using a small capillary tube containing a solution of the substance in a volatile solvent. The tip of the capillary is touched to the adsorbent at position F, Figure 2-8. Suitable solvents are methylene chloride, ether, and acetone. The solvent involved is allowed to evaporate after spotting the plate.

Up to three spots can be placed side by side on one microscope slide plate. The use of multiple spots on a plate as well as streaking instead of spotting on larger plates is described later.

3. Development of Chromatogram

The spotted microscope plate is now placed in the container C (Figure 2-8) containing the solvent. The choice of a suitable solvent is usually easily made if only a single component of the substance in question has an R_f (for example, if the remaining material is polymeric or so polar that it will not move readily). If a mixture of two or more substances is present, the choice of a solvent or solvent mixture may be facilitated as follows. On one plate make about five spots as described in section 2. Then allow small amounts of five different solvents to flow through small capillary tubes placed at each of the five spots. Thus a circle of solvent, with the original spot as the center, moves out for 1/4 to 1/2 in. depending on the amount of solvent allowed to flow. After drying the plate and treatment to enable visualization, the results illustrated in Figure 2-10 may be obtained (only three situations shown). The spot at (a) shows that no material has moved. Hence this solvent is unsuitable for use. The spot at (b) shows that all material, except a small amount of strongly held material, has moved with the solvent front. Hence, this solvent is also unsuitable. The spot at (c) seems ideal as it shows two

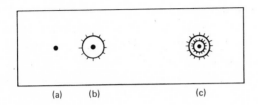

(a)　　(b)　　　　　(c)

Figure 2-10. Solvent testing for thin layer chromatography.

components which have separated reasonably well in moving only a short distance. By intelligent use of this technique much time may be saved in thin layer chromatography. Information thus obtained can be helpful in selecting solvents for crystallization and/or column chromatography.

In general, the following common solvents are listed in order of increasing polarity. Saturated hydrocarbons, CCl_4, benzene, CH_2Cl_2, $CHCl_3$, ether, ethyl acetate, acetone, lower alcohols, water.

4. Use of Thin Layer Chromatography in Following New Reactions

One of the most time-consuming aspects of carrying out a new reaction is deciding the length of time to allow the reaction to proceed before stopping it and isolating the products. Thin layer chromatography can help cut down the time in the following way.

Assume that the new reaction involves two organic reactants, I and II. By preliminary thin layer chromatography, the R_f value for each reactant can be determined in more than one solvent. Small samples of the reaction mixture are taken at varying times and spotted on plates, each of which has been spotted with pure I and II. Development of the plates then will indicate the presence or absence of I and II and the appearance of any new compound or compounds. Thus a great deal of information about the course of the reaction can be obtained which will facilitate decisions as to the proper way of achieving the desired result.

5. Use of Thin Layer Chromatography for Isolation of Compounds

If larger plates (about 7 × 7 in.) are used, a mixture can be spotted by streaking.

Consult reference [12] for details concerning application by streaking.

When a streaked plate is developed, the materials proceed in a line. After drying the line containing one component can be scraped off into a small sintered glass Buchner funnel and the adsorbed material can be eluted and thus isolated. In favorable cases as much as 50–150 mg of pure material can be isolated in this way by using one plate.

In conclusion, it is necessary to repeat and to emphasize that the order in which the various purification procedures should be applied varies from case to case. The order in which the procedures are described in this chapter may or may not be suitable for the purification of any particular mixture of solid components. Only experience allows an investigator to arrive at the best results in the least time.

REFERENCES

[1] Andrews, L. J. and R. M. Keefer, *Molecular Complexes in Organic Chemistry*, Holden-Day, Inc., San Francisco, 1964.

[2] von Briegleb, G., *Electronen-Donator-Acceptor-Komplexe*, Springer Verlag, Berlin, 1961.

[3] Orchin, M. and O. E. Woolfolk, *J. Amer. Chem. Soc.*, **68**, 1727 (1946).

[4] Orchin, M., L. Reggel, and O. E. Woolfolk, *J. Amer. Chem. Soc.*, **69**, 1225 (1947).

[5] Newman, M. S. and W. B. Lutz, *J. Amer. Chem. Soc.*, **78**, 2469 (1956).

[6] For a somewhat more elaborate apparatus for effecting smooth packing, see Dannley, R. L., and B. L. Weigand, *Anal. Chem.*, **31**, 1284 (1959).

[7] See Tipson, R. S., *Anal. Chem.*, **22**, 628 (1950) for an excellent account of the theory, scope, and methods of crystallization.

[8] Powell, H. M., *J. Chem. Soc.*, 2658 (1954).

[9] For example, see Maron, S. H., and C. F. Pruton, *Principles of Physical Chemistry*, 4th ed., The MacMillan Co., New York, 1965, pp. 382–391. Since aqueous systems are covered, substitute solvate for hydrate generally.

[10] Hershberg, E. B., *Ind. Eng. Chem., Anal. Ed.*, **8**, 312 (1936). A variety of other melting-point apparatus is described in most equipment catalogs.

[11] See Fieser, L. F., *Experiments in Organic Chemistry*, part II, D. C. Heath and Co., New York, 1941, p. 329. This book has many illustrations of useful laboratory aids.

[12] See Randerrath, K., *Thin Layer Chromatography*, Academic Press, New York, 1966; Bobbitt, James, *Thin Layer Chromatography*, Reinhold, New York, 1964; or Stahl, E., *Thin Layer Chromatography*, English ed., Academic Press, New York, 1965, for excellent treatments of thin layer chromatography.

Three

Adipic Acid-Ethanol Equilibrium

The objective of this experiment is to recover a minimum of 90% of diethyl adipate, ethyl hydrogen adipate, and adipic acid from an equilibrium mixture of adipic acid and ethanol.

$$HOOC(CH_2)_4COOH + C_2H_5OH \overset{H^+}{\rightleftharpoons}$$

$$HOOC(CH_2)_4COOC_2H_5 + H_2O$$

$$HOOC(CH_2)_4COOC_2H_5 + C_2H_5OH \overset{H^+}{\rightleftharpoons}$$

$$C_2H_5OOC(CH_2)_4COOC_2H_5 + H_2O$$

The technique involved is continuous extraction of a water-soluble compound from an aqueous solution by ether.

A solution of a given amount of adipic acid in a specified amount of absolute ethanol containing mineral acid is held at reflux until equilibrium has been established. A scheme must be designed by which the neutral and acidic components can be separated and then the two acidic components separated from each other. A number of points regarding this separation are considered below. In particular, the fact that a large amount of ethanol is present in the equilibrium mixture must be kept in mind.

If alkaline extraction is used to separate diethyl adipate from acidic components, the strength and amount of base used and the temperature of the extraction must be considered because diethyl adipate and ethyl hydrogen adipate are subject to alkaline hydrolysis. To the extent that this occurs, the proportions of products will be changed relative to those present at equilibrium. Since acid-catalyzed hydrolysis of organic esters is generally slower than alkaline hydrolysis, the alkaline extracts should be acidified soon after separation. The quantitative separation of ethyl hydrogen adipate and adipic acid is not too easily effected by any extraction into ether–benzene. The organic solvent extraction would have to be applied several times to the aqueous–alcoholic mixture in order to have most of the mono ester extracted into the ether–benzene layer. These extracts will contain some adipic acid also. If the ether–benzene extracts are washed with water to remove the dissolved adipic acid, then some mono ester is extracted into the aqueous phase.

Therefore, when you decide just when a suitable separation has been effected, there will be an ether–benzene layer which contains most of the monoethyl adipate and some adipic acid. This layer can be worked up and the mono ester distilled using the general procedure described in Chapter 1. One additional precaution is required to keep ethyl hydrogen adipate pure. This compound, m.p. 28°C, is hygroscopic and, if not carefully protected from moisture, will soon liquefy.

The best way to store hygroscopic compounds, or compounds which react slowly with moisture, oxygen, or carbon dioxide (many amines), is to seal them in glass ampoules. Material to be used later in a series of experiments is conveniently sealed in weighed ampoules which are reweighed after filling. Thus known amounts of such sensitive compounds can be available without opening and resealing stoppered containers. If large (250-, 500-, and 1000-ml) Pyrex ampoules are needed, they can be ordered from the Corning Glass Company. On occasion dioxane has been purified in large amounts for use in kinetic measurements and sealed in 500–1000-ml ampoules until ready for use. A sealed sample of α-bromophenylacetyl chloride, prepared in 1934, has not changed in appearance.

For short periods of time it may be kept in glass-stoppered bottles which have been ground-in as described for stopcock plugs of separatory funnels (see page 14). The stopper–bottle junction is then covered with molten paraffin by application with a brush. Such a bottle is best stored in a refrigerator. For the purpose of this experiment the purity of the sample can be gauged by appearance. If not really pure ethyl hydrogen adipate will not have a nice crystalline appearance.

Half esters should be used shortly after preparation because of disproportionation with time.

In order to isolate the adipic acid from the aqueous layer, continuous extraction with ether is recommended. This type of extraction is conveniently carried out in the apparatus shown in Figure 3-1. The solution A to be extracted in put into a tall wide-mouth bottle B which is a bit larger than required to hold the aqueous layer.

*Bottles with **T** necks as containers having proper dimensions are not generally available in glass apparatus catalogs. A round-bottomed or E flask is usable, but there is a much shorter path for the ascending ether droplets to traverse through the solution to be extracted, and*

Adipic Acid-Ethanol Equilibrium   **75**

hence extraction is slower. However, ℑ containers with suitable dimensions can easily be made.

The adapter C is put in place and connected to boiler flask D containing boiling stones and supported by the electric heating mantle E.

Liquids other than ether may be used in this apparatus as long as they are lighter than the solution to be extracted. Apparatus suitable for continuous extraction with liquids heavier than water is available [1].

Enough ether must be used so that, when the empty space F above the water level G is filled by distillation of solvent from D, there will

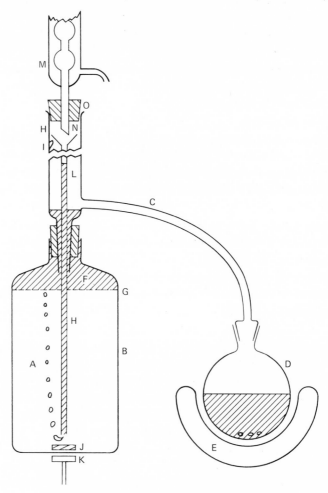

Figure 3-1. Continuous extraction apparatus.

still be sufficient solvent in D to boil evenly after the extracted material is transferred to D. The funnel H resting on the indentations I (three, evenly spaced), should be long enough that its tip will be located just above the bottom of the bottle or just above the path of a magnetic stirring bar J.

A magnetic stirrer K may be used to advantage to rotate a stirring bar J and thus make extraction a bit more rapid and complete.

The tip of the funnel should not rest on the bottom because only a small amount of solid on the bottom might block the flow of ether. The height L of ether in the funnel is determined by the height and the specific gravity of the liquid being extracted. In general there should be no more than a distance of 4 in. from the level G of the liquid being extracted to the bottom of the sidearm of C through which the solvent returns to D. Any efficient reflux condenser M will be satisfactory as long as it has a drip tip N so that the ether will flow through the funnel H. Either a 🅣 or neoprene closure at the top O is satisfactory.

As material is extracted from A and builds up in D, the level G of A in B drops. If marks are made at the initial and at subsequent levels, the progress of the extraction can be followed. When the level no longer drops, the extraction is complete.

In some cases the level G continues to drop a small amount after essentially all of the water-soluble components in A have been extracted to D. Also, in some cases an aqueous layer will separate in D and cover the boiling stones. If this happens the boiler flask should be replaced with another which contains fresh solvent so that smooth ebullition can be maintained.

The time required is mainly a function of the rate of distillation of ether and of the distribution coefficient of material being extracted between ether and water.

When the continuous extraction is completed, the ether is distilled and the residue worked up to produce pure adipic acid. If appreciable monoethyl adipate is present, it should be removed by vacuum distillation or extraction. The adipic acid can then be purified by crystallization.

Even though some materials may be extracted by ether (or other solvents) from aqueous solutions or suspensions by several hand extractions, continuous extraction may be preferable for the following reasons.

1. Less working time is required, since one merely has to assemble the apparatus and start the operation. While continuous extraction is taking place the operator is free to do other work.
2. The product at the end is in a smaller volume of solvent than it would be if several hand extractions were made.
3. In many hand extractions insoluble material hinders clean separation of layers and much time is lost (see page 15).
4. Higher recovery of materials is usually obtained.

It is frequently necessary to repeat the experiment in order to obtain the minimum of 90% of the three pure components. However, successful completion of this experiment carries with it a clear conviction that over 90% of reaction products may be accounted for, even in a difficult situation if the necessary technique is developed. A few students have isolated over 95% of the products.

Interestingly, even though each one of a class of from ten to fifteen students eventually achieves the goal, the amounts of each component reported may vary quite a bit. For example, in a particular year the yield of diethyl adipate may vary from 60 to 75%, the ethyl hydrogen adipate from 17 to 33%, and the yield of adipic acid from 0.2 to 4.2%. Yet in each case over 90% of the products have been isolated, supposedly starting with the same amounts of materials! When confronted with these facts, there is much wonderment. How can this be? Each student is sure his result is the correct one. All in all it is a very sobering experiment and makes the important point that one should never be satisfied with the results of a single experiment, no matter how well or carefully done. Furthermore, this experiment brings the conviction that extreme attention to detail is necessary if a person's work is to be duplicated by someone else or even by himself.

A class discussion concerning the possible causes for the individual members to fail to check each other's results is suggested.

REFERENCE

[1] Wiberg, K. B., *Laboratory Technique in Organic Chemistry*, McGraw-Hill Book Company, Inc., New York, 1960, p. 182.

Four

Vacuum Fractional Distillation

Two experiments, each of which involves the technique of vacuum fractional distillation, are described in this section: I, isolation of the methyl esters of the fatty acids in bayberry wax; and II, the preparation of chloroethylene carbonate. In addition, the technique of molecular distillation is described.

I. Preparation of Methyl Myristate and Methyl Palmitate from Bayberry Wax

The objective of this experiment is to isolate methyl myristate and methyl palmitate by vacuum fractionation of the methyl esters formed from bayberry wax.

The technique involved is fractional distillation under reduced pressure. The chemical reaction of transesterification is illustrated in the equation below.

$$
\begin{array}{l}
\text{CH}_2\text{OC(CH}_2)_n\text{CH}_3 \\
\quad\; \overset{\text{O}}{\overset{\|}{}} \\[4pt]
\text{CHOC(CH}_2)_n\text{CH}_3 + \text{CH}_3\text{OH} \underset{\text{excess}}{\overset{\text{HCl}}{\rightleftharpoons}} \text{CHOH} + 3\,\text{CH}_3(\text{CH}_2)_n\text{COOCH}_3 \\
\text{CH}_2\text{OC(CH}_2)_n\text{CH}_3
\end{array}
$$

The fatty acids present as esters in bayberry wax are converted into methyl esters by acid-catalyzed transesterification with methanol. By vacuum fractionation, methyl myristate and methyl palmitate are isolated. Since vacuum fractionation requires many hours, this experiment may be carried out by a group of three, one of whom is designated as group leader. The group leader should be responsible for organizing the work load, ensuring that the equipment to be used is in good condition before the lengthy fractionation is started, and seeing that the report is completed (see Chapter 12 for comments on report writing).

About 250 g of bayberry wax (mainly triglycerides of fatty acids) is dissolved in a suitable amount of absolute methanol containing sulfuric acid as catalyst. The solution is refluxed until equilibrium has been established. After cooling and diluting with water, the methyl esters formed are isolated using the ether–benzene extraction procedure described in Chapter 1. The ester fraction should be vacuum distilled as in Chapter 1 without attempting any fractionation. Such a distillation is always advisable before running a lengthy fractional distillation since impurities which may cause discoloration and undesirable side reactions are thus removed. The distillate should be heated (to decrease viscosity) and transferred *without solvent* to the distillation flask A (Figure 4-1) for fractionation.

Many different systems for vacuum fractionation have been used. Variations in all of the components of such systems have been numerous. By the use of electrical instrumentation, many operations can be automated. However, in most laboratory course work such systems are not available, and a relatively simple apparatus will be discussed.

The apparatus for vacuum fractionation is similar to that described in Chapter 1 for vacuum distillation except that a fractionation column and a fraction cutter are needed. Comments concerning the heating bath, distillation flask, fractionating column, fraction cutter, and vacuum system follow.

1. Heating Bath

A description of the setup of a heating bath is given on pages 23–24. For careful control of the lengthy heating required, a fused salt bath heated by an electric heating mantle which is controlled by a variable transformer and supported by a lab jack is recommended. Considerable time is needed to find out what temperature the heating bath will reach at different settings of the variable transformer; therefore, a few should be determined by experiment *before* the day chosen for the fractionation. The heating of the bath should be started the night before so that no time is lost in the morning in bringing the heating bath to the desired temperature. Knowledge of this temperature is gained from the vacuum distillation of the esters which has preceded the fractionation. A fused salt bath ($NaNO_2$–KNO_3) is preferred in this experiment because of the relatively high temperatures needed. Oils of various types discolor badly after repeated use.

2. Distillation Flask

A Claisen flask A with a suitable capillary leak B as shown in Figure 4-1 is recommended for vacuum fractionation. Alternatively, one may use adapters, as shown in Figure 4-2, for introducing heating coils into the liquid to be distilled [1]. When a suitable current is passed by means of the electric leads A through the coil of wire B

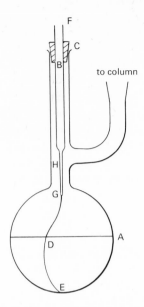

Figure 4-1. Modified Claisen flask for vacuum fractionation.

in the adapter C (see reference [1] for details of construction) the heat causes smooth ebullition. In practice we have found that the coil B becomes corroded with certain compounds and will cease to be effective. In this case a new coil can readily be affixed by using the connections at D.

In general the use of various solid boiling stones or wooden applicator rods has not proved advisable when lengthy vacuum fractionations are carried out because they often cease to function

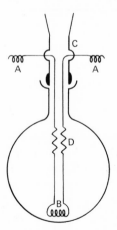

Figure 4-2. Adapter for introducing hot coil.

after a few hours. When this happens the fractionation must be interrupted.

The construction of a suitable capillary B for use as shown in Figure 4-1 requires a fair amount of skill. The following suggestions illustrated in Figure 4-3 should help to develop the ability to make such capillaries. A piece of 8-mm outside diameter (OD) Pyrex tubing about 1 ft long is heated by a flame adjusted so that about a 0.5-in. length, a, is heated as shown in stage I of Figure 4-3. A suitable flame can be obtained with a small glass-blowing hand torch clamped so that the flame can be directed upward conveniently. Tips are available to provide small pointed flames. The tube should be rotated fairly rapidly by hand so that the input of heat is as nearly uniform as possible. No problem is caused by unequal rotation by the right and left hands because, before melting occurs at the heated zone, the tube is rigid. However, as soon as melting begins an even rate of rotation by the right and left hands becomes important because the two halves rotate almost independently. Since there is a tendency for the tube to sag when melting begins, the two hands should be pushed together slightly so that the axes of the two side tubes are held at an angle. This will support the melted portion, as shown for stage II. The process of rotating the two ends and pushing slightly is continued until the situation pictured in stage III is

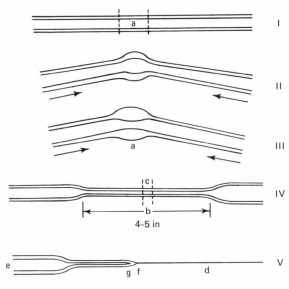

Figure 4-3. Construction of a capillary leak.

attained. Here, the thickness of the heated section is considerably greater than the original thickness, but the internal diameter should be almost as large as at the start. The tube is then taken out of the flame, the two halves aligned, and a small period of time (about 1–3 sec) allowed to elapse before the drawing out process. This drawing out is extremely important. If the drawing is too quick and for too great a distance, the result will be a tubing section b, stage IV, which is too thin-walled, too long, and of too small an internal diameter for the second part of the construction of the capillary. If the drawing is too slow (and it rarely is) the tubing section b will be too thick-walled, too short, and of too large an internal diameter. When properly carried out, the drawing will result in a drawn out portion which is about 4 to 5 in. long and has an internal diameter of about 3/4 to 1 mm and a tube thickness of about 1/2 to 3/4 mm, as shown in stage IV.

For the second part of the construction the flame of the burner must be made much narrower. Usually a smaller tip is needed. A narrow region c of stage IV is heated evenly all around and then pulled rapidly apart so that a very long and narrow capillary tube results as shown in Stage V. If properly made this capillary is 8–10 in. long and can be broken easily at any desired length by pressing with a thumb nail on the capillary held on a finger. The amount of heating at c, stage IV, and the rate of pulling are critical. If the heating at c is too great, the walls will collapse before the pulling stage. In this case pulling yields a fine solid rod but no capillary. If the heating has not been sufficient the resulting capillary will be too large and too stiff for effective use. The size of the capillary d can be readily gauged by placing the end of the capillary in a small test tube containing acetone or ether. The size of the bubbles produced in the solvent by blowing with the mouth held firmly at e can be observed. If the capillary leak is well made, the bubbles should be so small that they are difficult to see.

Should the capillary be unsatisfactory for any reason, break it off at f, stage V, and attach a glass rod handle by melting the rod and the part at f firmly together. Then heat a narrow portion at g, stage V, and try another pull. A fair amount of practice is needed before the feel is established, but once gained it will not be lost.

The capillary tube should now be put into the proper neoprene stopper C inserted into the neck of the Claisen flask, as shown in

Figure 4-1. The capillary length should be slightly less than the diameter of the flask and should bend about as shown at D when the neoprene stopper is forced down to the operating position. When properly positioned the tip of the capillary leak E will play about over an area at the bottom of the Claisen flask and ensure steady ebullition under reduced pressure for as long as needed. So little air actually comes through the capillary that no attention need be paid to this leak unless a very oxygen-sensitive substance is being handled. In this case a nitrogen-filled balloon may be attached at F.

The proper length for the capillary portion of the leak depends somewhat on its flexibility—itself a function of the drawing out process—the size of the flask, and the viscosity of the liquid to be distilled. The only precaution needed to ensure that the tip is not broken involves the short section G. A knock at this point will result in breakage. The portion H is reasonably strong, and the portion D is so weak that it will bend quite a bit before it breaks. However, when inserting the neoprene stopper care must be exercised that the tip near G does not hit the neck of the flask because breakage at G occurs very easily. When capillary leaks are prepared as described two should be available. It is advisable to fit both to the Claisen flask to be used; then if one is broken, the other may immediately be put into use.

After the liquid mixture to be fractionated has been transferred to the Claisen flask *do not put the stopper C (Figure 4-1) in place until ready to apply vacuum to the system.* If the capillary is inserted and left in the liquid for a few minutes before applying the vacuum, capillary forces cause the liquid to rise in the capillary tube. It may require many minutes before the liquid is sucked back so that air may enter the tip. Occasionally, the leak fails to operate at all.

The failure of a capillary leak to operate can be especially annoying if the fractionation must be interrupted during its course. In this event the alternative capillary should be inserted just before one reapplies the vacuum, and the starting capillary cleaned with solvent for later use if needed.

3. Fractionating Column

For vacuum fractionation of moderate amounts of material, columns such as that illustrated in Figure 4-4 have been used at Ohio State for many years. The column itself is a hollow glass tube

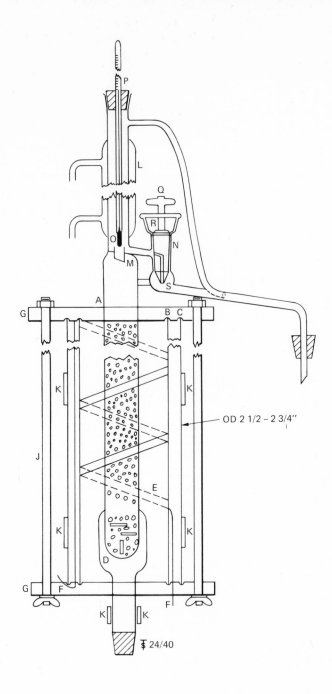

Figure 4-4. Vacuum fractionation column.

A, which has an internal diameter of $1\frac{1}{4}$ to $1\frac{1}{2}$ in. This column should be packed with glass beads of 3/16- to 1/4-in. diameter.

A study of various packing materials for vacuum fractionation has been made [2]. In accordance with the recommendation in this paper glass beads have been found very effective for separation of many different mixtures. Heligrid packing may become corroded if halogen-containing compounds are fractionated.

For fractionation of small to moderate amounts of material, spinning band columns are recommended. The magnetically-stirred models are preferable to mechanically-stirred models in our experience. A variety of such columns is available from the Nester Faust Corporation, Newark, Delaware.

The packed section is about 23–30 in. long and is surrounded with two concentric glass tubes B and C as shown. The internal diameter of B should be just large enough so that it can easily clear the wide bottom D of column A. The exterior of B is wrapped by a spiral of thin resistance ribbon E which is held out of direct contact with B by a number of vertical 1/2-in. strips of asbestos paper (not shown). These strips are conveniently held in place on B if they are wet and affixed while damp. They remain stuck to B so that wrapping the wire E is simplified. To the ends of the heating ribbon are attached leads F leading to a variable transformer so that the external heating of the column can be accurately controlled. Column C should have an internal diameter just sufficient to clear the heating spiral wrapped around B. The tubes B and C are held in place by two wooden supports G. The construction of these supports is shown in Figure 4-5.

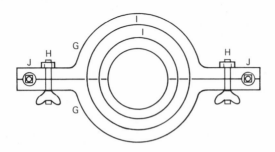

Figure 4-5. Wooden column heater supports.

The supports G are made from two equal halves clamped together by the metal butterfly nuts and bolts H. On the bottom of the top support and the top of the bottom support there are two circular grooves I cut to fit the tubes B and C. The top and bottom wooden supports G are held together by the long metal rods J, which are held in place by nuts as shown.

The column A and the tube C (Figure 4-4) are held in the proper position by the clamps K. The clamp holding the column A at the bottom should have asbestos paper between the column and the clamp (see page 32). The device D at the bottom of the column is designed to let a large amount of vapor go up the column, to support the beads used as packing, and to allow liquid to return to the distillation flask. The details of construction of D are shown in Figure 4-6. The rectangular vertical slots y in the bottom curved portion of the column are made with a glass cutting wheel and are about 3/4 in. long. This structure allows liquid to return mainly at the bottom. The vapor can go through the horizontal slots z just above. There is also an oval hole in the bottom so that no bead can seal it off.

The straight condenser L (Figure 4-4) at the top of the column should have an internal diameter of about 3/4 in. The water-cooled portion need not be longer than 6 in. The small ridge at M with the drip tip as shown leads to a Newman stopcock N [3]. The bulb O

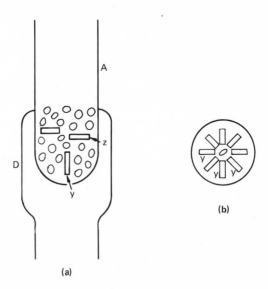

(a)

Figure 4-6. (a) Detail of bottom of column D. (b) View of bottom curved section looking up from distilling flask.

of the thermometer P should be located at least 1/2 in. below the water-cooled part of the condenser. The thermometer is easier to read if the scale is above the neoprene stopper which holds it firmly in place. The sidearm of the column is fitted to the fraction cutter shown in Figure 4-7.

Thermometers with the scales 8–10 in. from the bulb have been obtained from the Brooklyn Thermometer Company. Alternatively, newer thermometers with adjustable immersion devices are available.

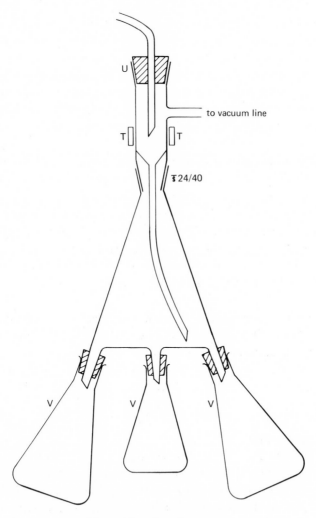

Figure 4-7. Fraction cutter.

4. Fraction Cutter

The fraction cutter (Figure 4-7) should be held firmly by clamp T so that no undue strain is put on the sidearm of the fractionating column when the lower portion is rotated in order to change receivers. For this reason a neoprene stopper is preferable to a ⚕ joint at the mouth of the adapter U, as more flexibility is attained. Receivers V with ⚕ joints are available but merely add expense and require more supports. When the vacuum is broken, a partly full ⚕ receiver may fall off unless held in place by a clamp. However, if neoprene stoppers which fit the receivers well are used, no clamps are needed. Only three receivers are shown in Figure 4-7. In practice fraction cutters having five or six receivers are used. It is more convenient to use E flasks in alternating sizes as receivers (up to and including 250 ml) since, when removed, they can be placed on any flat surface. Small E flasks (25 ml) are suggested for receiving foreruns and intermediate cuts in fractionation, as they should be small in volume if fractionation is carried out correctly (see page 97).

The prejudice against the use of E flasks for vacuum receivers probably stems from the fact that flat surfaces cannot withstand pressure as well as round surfaces. However, modern E flasks are so sturdy that there is no danger of collapse, even of a 250-ml flask. There are two disadvantages to the use of round-bottomed flasks as receivers: one, they occupy more space laterally and hence are more difficult to attach and detach; and two, after being disconnected they cannot stand by themselves but require a support.

Fraction cutters having only one receiving flask which may be changed any number of times during fractionation by proper manipulation of stopcocks can be used.

Apparatus catalogs may be consulted for a variety of fraction cutting devices.

5. Vacuum System

The system used to maintain constant pressure for vacuum fractionation should be carefully made and kept in good working order by constant attention. A setup similar to that described earlier (see page 31) is satisfactory. Probably the most important feature is the pressure regulator which must maintain a constant pressure during a run and which *must be able to deliver the same pressure if the fractiona-tion is interrupted and restarted.*

Vacuum Fractionation Procedure

1. Attainment of Equilibrium at Total Reflux

To start a vacuum fractionation equilibrium must first be estab-lished at total reflux (stopcock N of Figure 4-4 shut) under the pressure selected. Distill the mixture fairly rapidly by applying heat through the heating bath. The rising vapor comes in contact with the column packing and condenses. This process can be followed visually and heat should be applied as rapidly as possible without causing flooding. Flooding results when the descending liquid can-not return to the pot through the column end D, Figure 4-4 (or any part of the column) because the amount of vapor rising from the pot is so great that the flow of condensed liquid back to the pot cannot occur rapidly enough. Severe flooding dislodges the packing upwards into M and must be avoided. The design at D (shown in detail in Figure 4-6) is excellent for preventing flooding at this part. The seal of the wide part D to the column A should be made very carefully so that the internal diameter at the seal is *no smaller than the inside column diameter.*

Slight flooding at different parts of column A (Figure 4-4) will usually occur during the initial heating period. Such flooding can easily be stopped by judicious removal of the plug Q in stopcock N. The slight amount of air thus introduced will cause the flooding liquid in the column to return to the pot rapidly. For this reason, mercury should not be put in the well at R until the column is operating well. Actually, if the stopcock initially used is accurately ground in (see page 14), no mercury will be needed in the well R. Lubrication is best effected by coating the plug with the liquid being distilled or with a small amount of stopcock grease.

Flooding may also be eliminated by pressing a sponge moistened with cold water to the part of Claisen flask A (Figure 4–1) above the heating bath. This action decreases the amount of hot vapor being delivered into the column and thus enables the liquid to return to the pot more easily.

Some time can be saved in approaching equilibrium if heat is applied from the start to the column by the helical coil E. However, when equilibrium is nearly at hand the amount of heating applied through E should be reduced. In operation through the hours only enough heat should be applied via E to ensure that there is no heat loss through the jacket.

One can determine before the day of the fractionation what settings of the transformer attached to the leads of the heating coil E are needed to maintain the column A at the temperature expected for the various products to be separated. In cases where viscous materials are being separated, a small input of heat through E over the minimum necessary to prevent heat loss from the column is desirable to help avoid flooding.

The real purpose of the heating jacket is to help maintain thermal equilibrium between the vapor and liquid in the column (an ideal situation that is never really reached).

When the column operation has reached the point at which the liquid is refluxing into the condenser of the column head at as rapid a rate as possible without flooding, the fractionation can begin.

In practice there may be a small amount of a low-boiling forerun that should be collected in a small receiver flask. The amount may be so small that no boiling range need be recorded. The main object is merely to get rid of it.

At this point if there is a leak in the stopcock, which may be seen by a procession of small bubbles rising from the bore of the stopcock plug back up the tube leading from the stopcock to the column, mercury or the liquid being distilled should be put in the well at R. However, be sure that it is a leak and not a small amount of low-boiling material (flaming helps decide).

Many prefer to grease the stopcock plug Q as lubrication makes adjustment of the plug easier under vacuum (see later). However, if the stopcock is well ground in (see page 14) lubrication can be effected by using some of the liquid being distilled. If grease is used do not use so much that the small filed sections (a in Figure 4-8) are partly blocked as this may cause difficulty in adjusting the reflux ratio. These filed sections make fine adjustment of the reflux ratio much easier than if they are not introduced. Careful filing with a good triangular file will produce the slots a.

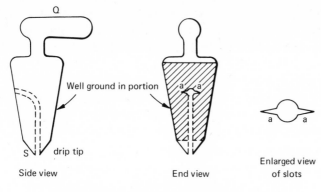

Figure 4-8. Detailed view of stopcock plug.

If mercury is used remember that the fraction cutter should be disconnected and a small beaker placed under the tip of the sidearm of the column to catch the mercury in the well when the plug is removed for cleaning after the fractionation has been completed.

2. Fractionation

Operations after equilibrium has been attained at total reflux must be guided by knowledge of the factors involved in fractional distillation. A typical vapor–liquid equilibrium curve for liquid A, boiling point T_1, and liquid B, boiling point T_2, at pressure P is shown in Figure 4-9. Assume that the mixture to be fractionated has the composition X. Then X_1 will be the composition of the vapor in equilibrium with the mixture at the intermediate temperature T_i,

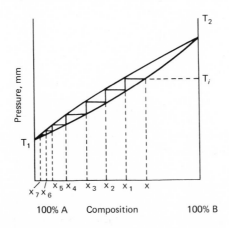

Figure 4-9. Vapor-liquid equilibrium diagram.

the boiling point of the mixture at this pressure. If distillation of a mixture of composition X were carried out in a flask so that *no fractionation could occur*, the composition of the first minute amount of distillate would have the composition X_1 (richer in the lower-boiling component that the original mixture). If distillation is continued, the composition of the liquid remaining in the pot would become richer in B until finally pure B would result. The composition of the distillate would also become richer in B and the temperature of the distillation would rise, eventually reaching T_2.

In a fractionation column, distillation is carried out so that vapor of constitution X_1 is condensed to liquid of composition X_1. As this liquid flows downward because of gravity, it is met by rising vapor of composition slightly richer in B than X. Part of the vapor rich in B is condensed by the cooler liquid of composition X_1. This condensation causes part of liquid X_1 to vaporize giving vapor of composition X_2. Similar processes occur as shown to give vapors richer in A until finally pure A is obtained. This qualitative description of what occurs in a fractionating column immediately makes clear two points: one, that there must be good contact between rising vapor and descending liquid; and two, that heat loss from (or heat input to) the column should be avoided. The second point can be accommodated easily by proper use of the heating coil E, Figure 4-4, as mentioned earlier. However, several factors must be considered with regard to item one.

Good contact between the vapor and liquid is provided by the construction and proper use of the column. Many different designs have been tested for varying liquid mixtures. Most of the laboratory manuals describe the operation of columns at atmospheric pressure. Relatively little, however, has been written about operation of fractionation columns under reduced pressure. Before running the fractionation of the methyl esters from bayberry wax (or any other vacuum fractionation), read the description of the studies made by the United States Bureau of Mines workers [2].

It is noteworthy that better results were attained at higher than at lower pressures. In general, the ratio of the vapor pressures of liquids A and B are greater at lower temperatures than at higher temperatures. This fact suggests that fractionation would be better at lower temperatures, hence at lower pressures. However, consider a compound of molecular weight 250, and a specific gravity of 1 at 127°C (400 A). One ml of the liquid yields about 1.3 liter of vapor at 760 mm, 13 liters at 76 mm, and 130 liters at 7.6 mm. Thus one can readily see why it is much more difficult to approach equilibrium between vapor and liquid at lower pressures. Furthermore, because of the greatly increased volume of vapor involved at low pressures, the mechanics of vapor and liquid flow require different packing for fractionation at atmospheric and reduced pressure.

In the situation depicted in Figure 4-9, it can be assumed that pure A would be obtained from liquid of composition X_7. Then, the column must have seven plates (a plate represents the theoretical enrichment in lower-boiling component resulting from a single vaporization and condensation) in order to produce a small amount of pure A from AB mixture of composition X.

One plate results from distillation from pot to column.

To be effective for the complete separation of A and B, it is obvious that the column must have several more plates for two reasons: one, as A is removed the composition of the remaining liquid rises along the lower liquid curve as it approaches pure B; and two, a column must have considerably more than the minimum number of plates in order that a distillation be completed in a reasonable time because columns never operate at 100% efficiency.

The efficiency of a column for a given separation is often expressed as HETP = height equivalent to a theoretical plate. The smaller the HETP, the greater the efficiency of the column. An idea of the relationship between boiling point differences of two liquids at atmospheric pressure and number of theoretical plates needed for separation is available [4].

When the equilibrium has been reached at total reflux, the temperature at thermometer P (Figure 4-4) should be noted. The plug Q of stopcock N should then be adjusted so that the liquid just begins to drop from the tip S. One can then make the first measurement of the reflux ratio, that is, the ratio of the number of drops at the drip tip below M to the number at S. At the start this should be high—at least 30/1. The higher the reflux ratio, the less the equilibria throughout the column are disturbed; hence, the more nearly the column operates at peak efficiency. However, the higher the reflux ratio, the slower the rate of obtaining distillate. Hence, it is necessary to determine the best reflux ratio to use at various points in the fractionation procedure.

The advantage of the Newman stopcock over straight bore stop-cocks in decreasing the time required to ascertain reflux ratios is the main reason for their use in fractionation heads. When an adjustment of the stopcock is made, the difference in rate of delivery of liquid at the plug tip S is immediately measurable. With a conventional stop-cock one must wait until the flow rate is adjusted to the entire length of the sidearm of the column so that the rate of delivery can be seen at the tip. The use of file marks, a, Figure 4-8, allow for finer adjust-ment of liquid delivery rate.

As the collection of distillate is started, the rate at which distilla-tion is allowed to occur depends upon the efficiency of the column, the boiling points of the substances being distilled, and the degree of purity desired for the fractions. Practically, the temperature gives the best criterion for controlling the reflux ratio. If the temperature remains constant at an initial reflux ratio of 30/1, try lowering to 20/1. If the temperature still remains constant, continue to lower the reflux ratio as long as the temperature does not rise. The possible situations are easily understood by considering a plot of milliliters of distillate versus temperature as shown in Figure 4-10. Assume that T_1 is the true boiling point of the first low-boiling component A.

Actually at the beginning of take-off there may be a fairly rapid rise in boiling point because of the removal of low-boiling components. The diagram in Figure 4-10 implies that all low-boiling components have been collected in a small forerun.

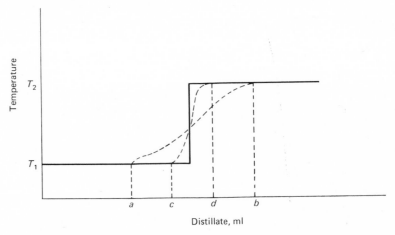

Figure 4-10. Plot of boiling point versus milliliters of distillate.

It might be determined by trial that even at a fairly low (for example, 5–8) reflux ratio the temperature remains constant while a large fraction is being collected. This means that the column has sufficient plates to separate the mixture at hand when not operating at maximum efficiency. However, a point (*a* on Figure 4-10) is reached when the temperature starts to rise. If the distillation is continued at the same reflux ratio, the boiling point of the second component will not be reached until a fairly large intermediate cut *a–b*, has been collected. However, if the reflux ratio is increased to about 15–20, the temperature will fall to T_1 and an appreciable amount of A can be collected until the temperature again starts to rise as at *c*. The intermediate cut, if taken at the 15–20 reflux ratio, is now smaller (*c–d*) than before. By increasing the reflux to 25–30 an even smaller intermediate cut might be obtained. Of course, the higher the reflux ratio, the better the separation but the longer the time needed. After consideration of these factors, the operation in a given vacuum fractionation must be decided.

With the column described methyl myristate can be separated from methyl palmitate with an intermediate fraction of 3–5 g without undue trouble.

If it is known that there is no higher-boiling component than compound B, it is not necessary to distill much B through the column. As soon as the boiling point of pure B has been reached and a reasonable amount has been collected (to be sure the boiling point remains constant), the fractionation may be stopped, the material in the column rinsed down by refluxing some solvent, and the remaining B distilled rapidly without any attempt at fractionation.

On the other hand, when a higher-boiling component than B is present in a quantity so small that the column will have insufficient liquid to operate properly after most of B has been distilled, a still higher-boiling component may be added at the start to act as a "chaser." In the present experiment for example, 30–40 g of methyl stearate might be added. Then all of the methyl palmitate can be distilled by using the technique for fractionation described. A "chaser" should be a compound that will not form an azeotope with the other components. Hence a compound of similar structure and functional group should be chosen.

After the fractionation, the materials should be put in suitable labeled containers and the distillation apparatus carefully cleaned.

II. The Preparation of Chloroethylene Carbonate

The objective of this experiment is to prepare pure chloroethylene carbonate by vacuum fractional distillation of the products of chlorination of ethylene carbonate.

Ethylene carbonate is photochemically chlorinated [5] in the apparatus illustrated in Figure 4-11 according to the following equations.

$$
\begin{array}{c}
CH_2O \\
\ | \quad\quad\ CO \\
CH_2O
\end{array}
+ Cl_2 \xrightarrow{hv}
\begin{array}{c}
CH_2O \\
\ | \quad\quad\ CO \\
ClCHO
\end{array}
+ HCl
$$

$$
\begin{array}{c}
CH_2O \\
\ | \quad\quad\ CO \\
ClCHO
\end{array}
+ Cl_2 \xrightarrow{hv}
\begin{array}{c}
ClCHO \\
\ | \quad\quad\ CO \\
ClCHO
\end{array}
+ HCl
$$

A weighed amount (about 300 g) of freshly vacuum-distilled molten ethylene carbonate A is charged into the outer jacket B which is held at the desired temperature (near 70°C) by the glycerine bath C contained in beaker D warmed by heater E. The low-pressure mercury resonance lamp [6], which consists of an evacuated quartz U-tube F fused by graded seals G to pyrex tops H containing the fused-in electrodes I, is turned on and the addition of chlorine through the tube J leading to the fritted glass disc K is commenced. It is desirable to have a tube leading from the exit L in order to be able to estimate the rate of formation of hydrogen chloride.

The evolution of hydrogen chloride may be observed by waving a small beaker containing concentrated ammonium hydroxide near the exit tube. The size of the white cloud of ammonium chloride produced is used as a guide. If a more accurate test is desired, a solution containing a known amount of sodium hydroxide and an indicator is used to trap the hydrogen chloride. When the solution changes to the acid color, the amount of acid that has been produced is known. This technique avoids venting hydrogen chloride from the hood exhaust and may also be used to advantage in following the progress of Friedel–Crafts reactions.

The flow of chlorine is regulated so that the evolution of hydrogen chloride is quite brisk but little free chlorine is lost. The progress of the reaction can be estimated conveniently by weighing the chlorination apparatus from time to time. For a 300-g run, the chlorination

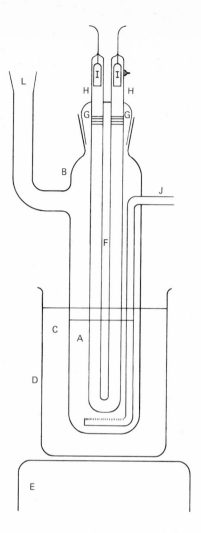

Figure 4-11. Chlorination apparatus.

is stopped after a gain in weight of about 115–120 g. Periods of 2–8 hr are needed for completion, depending on rate of addition of chlorine. The chlorination need not be effected in one continuous operation; it may be interrupted as frequently as desired. Some attention is required to maintain the reaction temperature near 70°C, but the reaction is not appreciably exothermic.

After the desired increase in weight has been effected, the crude mixture is transferred to a Claisen flask (see page 23) and rapidly vacuum distilled.

Since hydrogen chloride is evolved, a good vacuum pump should not be used. The vacuum produced by a good water pump (10–15 mm) is sufficient for this distillation.

The distillate, which is almost colorless, is placed in a modified Claisen flask (see Figure 4-1, page 82) for fractionation as described in part I of this chapter. It is better to use a pressure in the 7–10 mm range rather than a lower pressure for this fractionation because of the relatively low boiling point of dichloroethylene carbonate. The low-boiling component (about 65°C at 7 mm) is a mixture of the cis and trans forms of dichloroethylene carbonate. The main fraction (boiling point about 95°C at 7 mm) is chloroethylene carbonate.

Chloroethylene carbonate should not be stored for more than a few days before use because it decomposes on standing.

When the temperature of the distillate begins to rise above the boiling point of chloroethylene carbonate at a high reflux ratio, the distillation should be terminated as the residue is mainly ethylene carbonate. There should be sufficient of this so that it can act as a "chaser" (see page 97).

The addition of about 40 g of ethylene carbonate before the fractionation is begun is advisable in order to be sure that sufficient ethylene carbonate is present to act as a chaser.

After cooling the ethylene carbonate remaining in the flask can be recovered by distillation. The various fractions should be weighed and put in suitable labeled containers. The distillation column should be cleaned thoroughly by distilling acetone into it.

Another experiment in which the use of vacuum fractional distillation is helpful in separating the products involves treatment of 1,3-dibromopropane with one equivalent of sodium cyanide [7]. In this experiment the 1,3-dibromopropane, 4-bromobutyronitrile, and glutaronitrile are readily separated on a good column. Glutaronitrile (mol. wt. 94) is the highest-boiling component, 4-bromobutyronitrile (mol. wt. 148) is intermediate, and 1,3-dibromopropane (mol. wt. 202) is the lowest.

In part II, ethylene carbonate (mol. wt. 88) is the highest boiling component, chloroethylene carbonate (mol. wt. 122.5) is intermediate, and dichloroethylene carbonate (mol. wt. 157) is the lowest. What is the explanation for these facts?

Molecular Distillation

The purification of compounds by means of molecular distillation is advantageous whenever the compound to be purified is thermally sensitive, that is, when the compound suffers rearrangement or decomposition and cannot be vacuum distilled unchanged by conventional techniques.

In molecular distillation, the condensing surface is located at a position less than the mean free path from the surface of the substance being distilled. The mean free path of a compound is the average distance traversed by a molecule between collisions. The principle involved in molecular distillation is the following. Consider the surface of a liquid at atmospheric pressure. Energy-rich (in a statistical sense) molecules do not escape from the surface because they are unable to travel far before colliding with gas molecules. These collisions rob the energy-rich molecules of energy, and the molecules return to the surface of the liquid. In other words, the mean free path is too small to permit the molecules of liquid which have vaporized to reach a condenser surface like that present in a conventional distillation apparatus. However, as the pressure over a liquid is decreased, the number of collisions decreases and the mean free path increases. When pressures in the range from 10^{-4} to 10^{-5} mm of mercury are attained, the mean free paths of many organic molecules lie in the 4–10 cm region. By placing a condensing surface within the mean free path, it becomes possible to distill liquids at 20–50°C, a range in which many sensitive compounds are thermally stable [8]. Many different designs for molecular distillation apparatus have been described [8]. For rapid molecular distillation on a moderate scale, the apparatus shown in Figure 4-12 is recommended as being relatively simple and easy to operate.

This design was originally suggested to me by Dr. Hickman in the early 1940s.

The liquid A to be submitted to molecular distillation is transferred with a minimum of solvent to the still B which contains a

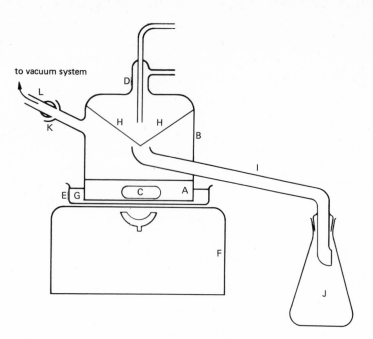

Figure 4-12. Molecular still.

glass- or Teflon-coated magnetic stirring bar C. The still is clamped at the water-cooled condenser D so that it rests just above, but not

Teflon coating is preferred because less breakage occurs.

touching, the flat crystallizing dish E, which is supported by a combination hot plate–stirrer F and contains a liquid heat transfer agent, for example, glycerol, G. If the liquid to be distilled is expected to come over rapidly at room temperature an apparatus without the water cooled condenser section D must be used. In such cases, the condenser surface H is cooled by ice or dry ice–isopropyl alcohol. The take-off arm I is fitted with a suitable receiver J which may be modified to allow for collection of several fractions. The still is connected to a suitable high-vacuum system at the balljoint K.

A typical high-vacuum system is shown in Figure 4-13. The tube L which connects to the still at K leads into the trap M which is similar to the trap shown in Figure 1-8, page 28 except all tubes are at least 1 cm internal diameter. This trap is connected to a vacuum gauge N, preferably of the McLeod type, calibrated to indicate pressures in the range from 10^{-2} to 10^{-5} mm. This gauge is con-

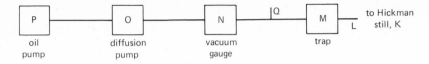

Figure 4-13. High-vacuum system.

nected to a diffusion pump O backed by a good mechanical pump P. There should also be a high-vacuum type stopcock Q provided so that air (or inert gas) may be introduced into the system when desired. The system shown in Figure 4-13 should have as few joints as possible, and the internal diameter of all connections should be at least 1 cm.

Consult apparatus catalogs for choices of vacuum gauges, diffusion pumps, and high-vacuum stopcocks.

In a typical operation, the magnetic stirring is started at a slow rate and the system is evacuated slowly so that the removal of most of the solvent will not cause bumping or frothing. The vacuum supplied by a good water pump directly connected at K is recommended for this operation and heating is unnecessary. After about 20–30 min, the water pump is disconnected and the main vacuum system is connected at K. The removal of solvent is continued for 10–15 min under the vacuum supplied by the vacuum pump only. Before starting the diffusion pump, the rate of magnetic stirring may be slightly increased. After the diffusion pump has been in operation for about 30–40 min, the first reading of pressure on the McLeod gauge N is made. If the pressure is not less than about 10^{-3} mm a leak tester should be played over the entire setup to see if a leak is involved.

The advice of a professional glass blower is invaluable in detecting leaks until experience is gained.

The time required to attain pressures of 10^{-4}–10^{-5} mm depends upon the absence of leaks, the complete removal of solvent from the distilland, and the efficiency at which the diffusion pump O works.

Experience with regard to the rate of heat input into the boiler of O must be gained.

When stirring is provided the time to reach the desired pressure is greatly reduced over the time required if stirring (or, in other apparatus, other types of liquid movement) is not provided. The reason for this is that molecules of liquid must be at the surface in order to go into the vapor phase. If there is no stirring, there is no rapid way for energy-rich molecules to get to the surface after the energy rich molecules which were originally there have gone into the vapor phase. The process is essentially diffusion controlled. In a viscous liquid, this diffusion can be extremely slow. For example, without stirring it may take 24 hr before the solvent is completely removed. If an attempt is made to speed up solvent removal by raising the temperature (without stirring), a sudden violent bump will cause the distilland to splash up in the apparatus. The entire procedure must then be repeated after tedious recovery of distilland. However, with stirring, solvent removal is usually complete within 1 hr after the diffusion pump is put into effective operation.

When the pressure is low enough, the condensation of distillate on the condenser surface can be seen. Once condensation occurs, the rate at which molecular distillation should be carried out depends on the materials at hand. A very slow rate can be increased to almost any desired rate by heating, provided that the thermal sensitivity of the product does not limit the temperature.

If heating seems desirable, be sure to raise the temperature extremely slowly to avoid bumping which may occur, even in a stirred still, if heating is too rapid.

A certain amount of fractionation can be accomplished in a molecular still by careful control of temperature if enough time is allowed. For example, one might collect all of the material that will distill when the bath temperature is no higher than 25°C. By raising the temperature to 35°, another fraction might be collected, and so on. However, if fractionation is desired, a different type of molecular still is preferable [8].

One very desirable feature of molecular distillation is that there is absolutely no entrainment (see page 35). Thus, in one distillation colorless (or pure colored) material is obtained even from a black mixture. For this reason, analytical samples of liquids are often purified by molecular distillation (in suitable small scale apparatus).

When the molecular distillation has been completed, the heater of the diffusion pump O is turned off, and shortly thereafter the mechanical pump P. An inert gas, or air, is then allowed to enter through stopcock Q. It is advisable to clean out the still and trap immediately after use.

REFERENCES

[1] Feldman, J., and P. Pantages, *Anal. Chem.*, **24**, 432 (1952).

[2] Myles, M., J. Feldman, I. Wender, and M. Orchin, *Ind. Eng. Chem.*, **43**, 1452 (1951).

[3] Newman, M. S., *Ind. Eng. Chem.*, **14**, 902 (1942).

[4] K. B. Wiberg, *Laboratory Technique in Organic Chemistry*, McGraw-Hill Book Company, Inc., New York, 1960, p. 44.

[5] Newman, M. S., and R. Addor, *J. Amer. Chem. Soc.*, **75**, 1263 (1953); **77**, 3789 (1955).

[6] See Calvert, Jack G., and James N. Pitts, Jr., *Photochemistry*, John Wiley and Sons, Inc., New York, 1966, p. 751, and Kharasch, M. S., and A. N. Friedlander, *J. Org. Chem.*, **14**, 239 (1949) for descriptions of other types of mercury lamps. The lamp used most frequently here is that described by Henne, A. L., and E. G. DeWitt, *J. Amer. Chem. Soc.*, **70**, 1548 (1948).

[7] Schlatter, M. J., *J. Amer. Chem. Soc.*, **63**, 1734 (1941).

[8] For a more complete discussion of molecular distillation and the equipment used see A. Weissberger, *Techniques of Organic Chemistry*, Interscience Publishers, John Wiley and Sons, Inc., New York, 2nd ed., 1965, chaps. VI and VII.

Five

Synthesis of Mesitylene

The object of this experiment is to synthesize mesitylene by reacting 3,3,5-trimethylcyclohexanone with methylmagnesium bromide, dehydrating the resulting alcohol to tetramethylcyclohexenes, and aromatizing the olefins to mesitylene by passing over a chromia-on-alumina catalyst in the vapor phase [1].

The techniques involved are the formation of Grignard reagents and vapor-phase reactions. This experiment should be a group effort, and the same comments apply as in Chapter 4.

Preparation of the Grignard Reagent

1. General

The formation of a Grignard reagent requires the reaction of an organic halide with magnesium metal in a solvent. The recommended apparatus, shown in Figure 5-1, consists of a three-necked flask A fitted with an efficient reflux condenser B, a stirrer C, and a pressure-equalizing dropping-funnel D. The reflux condenser should have a drip tip E, so that the rate of reflux can be judged, and a capillary diffusion tube F at the top [2]. The pressure-equalizing addition-funnel shown [3] is especially useful in larger sizes when pear-shaped separatory funnels would interfere with the stirrer shaft. When an inert gas is needed, it may be introduced through the top G of the addition funnel.

An Advanced Organic Laboratory Course

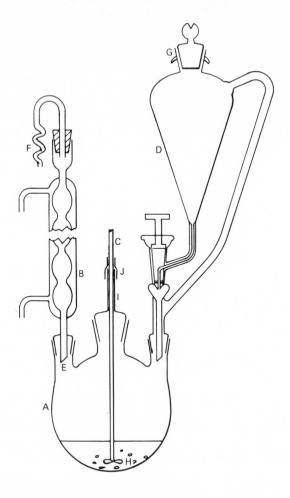

Figure 5-1. Apparatus for preparation of Grignard reagents.

Many types of stirring rods and bearings can be used. The stirring rod C shown in Figure 5-1 is all glass and has a propellor-type structure H at the working end. Such stirrers are inexpensive but, because there is no flexibility at the working end, the size of H is limited by the size of the center neck (preferably ℑ 40/50). For the formation of Grignard reagents this limitation is not important, as vigorous stirring is unnecessary. More flexibility in stirring rods is attainable with two-piece assemblies; these include a rod and a Teflon paddle which can be affixed.

Consult apparatus catalogs for examples of such stirring devices.

For bearings I, many stirrers are available in which the stirring rod and bearing are carefully ground. These have the advantage that almost no leakage of gas out, or air in, occurs. However, they have the disadvantage of being expensive and difficult to align with the stirring motor shaft. If alignment is not perfect, vibration of the entire setup is often excessive. If the sizes of home-made unground shafts C and bearings I are carefully chosen, only a small amount of play will be involved. Placement of a short length of rubber tubing J, as shown, provides for smooth stirring and protects against leakage of air or gas at this juncture. The tubing J is chosen so that it just fits C at the contact point which is lubricated with glycerine.

Metal stirrers may also be used but for Grignard reactions are not necessary or desirable. (See page 127 for further discussion.)

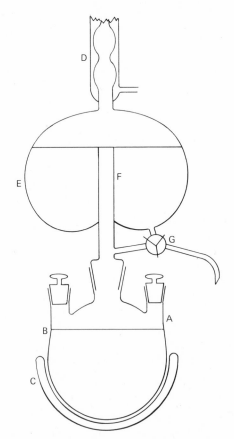

Figure 5-2. Apparatus for purification of ether for grignard reagents.

Diethyl ether is generally the best solvent for use in the formation of Grignard reagents. The best way of purifying ether for Grignard-reagent formation is to distill it over preformed Grignard reagent, using the apparatus shown in Figure 5-2. About 1 mole of butyl-magnesium bromide in 1 liter of ether is prepared in the 5-liter flask A (or transferred to it). Dry ether is prepared by allowing a good grade of ether (about 99.5 % ether + 0.5 % water, commercially available) to stand over calcium hydride (or a desiccant) for several days. The dry ether is added until the flask A is about 4/5 full (level B). Any impurity in this ether (especially peroxides) reacts with the Grignard reagent and is either destroyed or converted to nonvolatile products. When heated by the heating mantle C, ether distills into the efficient reflux condenser D and is collected in the adapter flask E which has a wide internal overflow tube F. The amount of ether required may then be tapped off through the three-way stopcock G. This set-up for ether distillation is convenient because of the overflow return feature at F. A convenient volume for the adapter flask is about 2 liters so that about 1.5 liters of ether is collected when filled to the level allowed by F. From time to time, more Grignard reagent is added as needed through a side neck of flask A.

The apparatus shown in Figure 5-2 is also suitable for the similar preparation of pure tetrahydrofuran. Lithium aluminum hydride may be used in place of Grignard reagents but is more dangerous when disposal is necessary.

Ether or tetrahydrofuran which has been standing around a laboratory for appreciable lengths of time should never be distilled to dryness unless one knows that peroxides are absent. The build up in concentration of ether peroxides by distillation of old solvent can lead to a violent explosion. Peroxides may be tested for by shaking a portion of the solvent in question with acidified sodium iodide solution. A brown-to-violet color indicates the liberation of iodine and hence the presence of peroxides.

The halides used for preparation of Grignard reagents should be pure and dry. If the halide used is prepared, the crude halide should be washed in a separatory funnel, at some stage in the purification, with sulfuric acid as concentrated as the halide will allow. Such washings remove alcohols, ethers, and olefins which might contaminate the halide. Commercial halides also may benefit from washing with acid.

The magnesium used for preparation of Grignard reagents is satisfactory for use as purchased and is placed directly in flask A which should be clean and dry.

Ordinary magnesium contains varying small amounts of impurities so that when the Grignard reagent has been prepared, the solution is usually dark colored. When pure sublimed magnesium is used, the Grignard solutions are almost colorless. The behavior of these two different types of Grignard reagents is often appreciably different.

The literature often recommends that the air in the flask A should be displaced with nitrogen before attempting to form the Grignard reagent. However, if ethylene dibromide is used in starting the reaction, nitrogen is unnecessary because ethylene is formed and effectively removes all air from the apparatus [4].

Initiation of the reaction between a halide and magnesium is no longer any problem if ethylene dibromide is used. Cover the magnesium with sufficient dry ether so that, when the exothermic reaction starts, the magnesium will not go dry. Add a small amount of the halide to be used without starting the stirrer. If there is no sign of the reaction starting (as observed by noting that several of the pieces of magnesium start to oscillate), about 1–2 ml of ethylene dibromide is added from an eyedropper. Within 30 sec a vigorous reaction commences and ethylene is produced. Once the reaction has started, a solution of the halide in ether should be added at such a rate that there is rapid reflux in condenser B (Figure 5-1).

If the rate of addition is too rapid and the flask A must be cooled to prevent too violent ebullition, care must be taken not to cool for so long that the reaction stops. The need to restart the reaction may cause much delay.

After all of the halide solution has been added from D (Figure 5-1), the resulting solution should be held at reflux for 10–20 min to ensure completion of the reaction. An excess of magnesium is usually advisable. If only one equivalent of magnesium to one of halide is used, completion of the reaction requires a fairly long time. For most uses an excess of magnesium is not harmful.

The Grignard reagent thus prepared is ready for use. If the yield of Grignard reagent is to be determined, aliquots are removed for titration [5]. For most halides, the yield is $90 \pm 5\%$.

Whether the Grignard reagent should be added to the compound in question, or vice-versa, can usually best be decided after both procedures have been tried. From the point of view of simplicity, addition of a solution of the compound in a suitable solvent to the Grignard reagent is preferable. However, the yield of desired product may be better if the Grignard reagent is added to the other reactant. Should this be the case, the Grignard reagent should be transferred to a separatory funnel or other container.

To effect such a transfer the reflux condenser B, stirrer C, and separatory funnel D (Figure 5-1) are removed from flask A containing the Grignard reagent and A is fitted as shown in Figure 5-3. A bent tube K is inserted through a well-fitting glass tube L over which there is a glycerine-lubricated short length of rubber tubing M (as described for J, Figure 5-1). The neoprene stoppers N, O, and P should be firmly fitted so that they will not be dislodged under the pressure which will be used. The tip of K should be fitted with some glass wool Q which is held in place by a tightened loop of wire R as shown. Alternately, a fritted glass tip may be used. The other end S of K is placed in the top of the container D which is to hold the Grignard reagent. There should be a sufficient length of K above S so that, when the tip at Q is pushed down to the bottom of flask A at the end of the transfer, the tube K will not hit the top of D. A

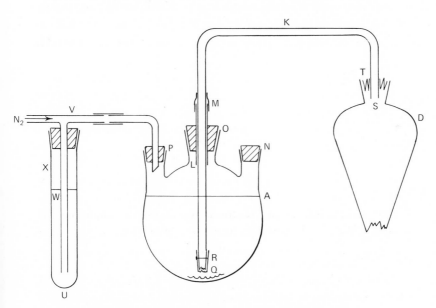

Figure 5-3. Apparatus for transfer of grignard reagents.

loose plug of cotton T is sufficient protection during the transfer. When the apparatus is firmly clamped, the introduction of nitrogen is begun. The use of a safety pressure regulator U is advised. This consists of a T-tube V, one length of which is long as shown, which dips into mercury W in a long test tube X. Thus, the maximum pressure attainable in the flask A is controlled by the height of the mercury in X.

The safety valve shown is useful whenever a gas under pressure is introduced into a reaction setup. The device makes it possible to be sure that, if there is a stoppage of flow of gas for any reason, the maximum pressure will be determined by the height of the mercury in the regulator.

At the start of the transfer, the end of tube K at Q should not be too close to the bottom. Often a certain amount of solid is mixed with the unused magnesium. If the end of the tube dips into this solid, the glass wool becomes plugged (in part, or sometimes completely). The transfer would thus be too slow. Most of the transfer can be effected when the tip is as shown in Figure 5-3. Near the end of the transfer, the tip can be pushed to the bottom because of the flexible arrangement provided at M.

In a study of the reaction of a Grignard reagent with some compound, it is often advisable to prepare a large quantity of Grignard reagent in one batch and transfer to a large bottle. Aliquots of the same Grignard reagent can then be used to test variables in reaction conditions. Much time is saved over the alternate procedure of making up fresh Grignard reagent for each run. If a large amount of Grignard reagent is prepared for such a study, the concentration should be close to 1-molar (M), as in more concentrated solutions crystallization of Grignard complexes may occur.

The procedure described for making Grignard reagents is satisfactory in most cases. However, if the halide used is allylic or benzylic, the yield is often quite low as coupling occurs [6]. The apparatus shown in Figure 5-4 is very useful for the preparation of allylic and benzylic Grignard reagents in high yield.

This method was originally described in the M.S. thesis presented by D. Rowlands, to The Ohio State University, 1948, under the supervision of Dr. K. Greenlee and Professor C. E. Board. A talk on it was

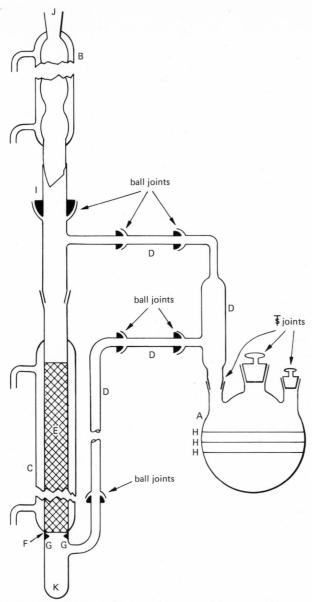

Figure 5-4. Apparatus for preparation of allylic and benzylic grignard reagents.

presented to the Organic Division of the American Chemical Society at the 117th National meeting, April, 1950, in Philadelphia, Pa. I am indebted to Dr. K. Greenlee for supplying directions for the apparatus and procedure.

This apparatus consists of a three-necked boilup flask A attached to an efficient reflux condenser B and a water-cooled reaction tube C by suitable connecting tubes D which have spherical joints to increase flexibility and hence ease of assembly. Magnesium turnings E (a large excess must be used) are placed in the reaction tube and are held in place by a small piece of wire gauze F held in place by three indentations G at a spot just below the cooling section. The dimensions of the reaction tube are governed by the size of the runs likely to be made.

For about 100 g of magnesium a volume of about 300 ml is required. In practice two assemblies having quite different capacities are useful. The inside diameter of smaller reactors is about 3/4 to 1 in.

A solution of mercuric chloride in dry ether (about 50 g/liter) is poured into C so that the level of the ether just covers the magnesium. The appearance of the magnesium should undergo no further change after standing overnight. This ether is then rinsed out by boiling dry ether from an ordinary one-necked round-bottomed flask. After boiling for a while any mercuric and magnesium chloride in C is transferred to the round bottom flask. A three-necked boilup flask A is now attached. This flask should have markings H (they may be etched on) which indicate known volumes of solution.

When aliquots are taken after the Grignard reagent has been made these markings facilitate estimation of the yield.

A suitable amount of dry ether is then placed in A, and distillation at a rapid rate (observed from the drip-tip at I) is started. The addition of the halide at J (usually diluted with a small amount of ether) from a pressure-equalizing dropping-funnel [3] is started. As reaction with the amalgamated magnesium takes place, the temperature in the reaction tube C rises. The flow of water through the condenser on C should be regulated so that there is no ebullition in C. The water flow will depend on the halide used and its rate of addition. As the Grignard reagent is formed under the high dilution conditions in C, it is swept into A and accumulates there. If sludge forms (often in cases where chlorides are used), much of it settles in the K portion. The volume of ether in the system is essentially constant so that the level of ether in A increases but slightly during a run. If the flow of cold water in the condenser which cools C is too rapid, the reaction may stop; care must be taken not to err in this respect.

Occasionally it is desirable to poke the magnesium by inserting a long stout wire from J in order to prevent channeling or plugging.

As the reaction proceeds the magnesium is used up. The amount of halide used determines the amount of Grignard reagent formed, as the yields are mostly over 95 %. If a series of reactions with allylic halides are contemplated, a large reaction tube C is desirable because several runs may be made using the same reaction tube. After the addition of halide from J is stopped, a short period of reflux washes all of the Grignard reagent from C into A. Addition of dry ether up to one of the premarked levels H completes the preparation. One can then fit the flask A with a stirrer, reflux condenser, and dropping funnel and proceed as desired.

This procedure has also been used to make the Grignard reagent from 1-bromo-2-heptyne in 98 % yield [7].

An apparatus recommended for the preparation of vinyl magnesium chloride in tetrahydrofuran has been described [8].

Preparation of Methylmagnesium Bromide

In the present experiment, a different technique for adding the halide must be used since methyl bromide (bp 3.6°) is a gas and comes in containers which are under pressure at room temperature.

Methyl iodide is more convenient to use because it is a liquid; however, it is much more expensive.

The amount of methylmagnesium bromide formed is regulated by the weight of magnesium used rather than by an attempt to weigh a quantity of methyl bromide. Methyl bromide from a cylinder of methyl bromide is introduced through a tube in neck K (Figure 5-1). The entering methyl bromide does not escape from the reflux condenser at F because it is soluble in ether and thus is returned in B and reacts with the magnesium. It is unnecessary (and undesirable because of blockage of the delivery tube) to have the top of the delivery tube dip under the surface of the ether in A. The entire amount of ether should not be introduced into flask A at the start because the solution of methyl bromide in ether would be too dilute. About 1/4 to 1/3 the amount of ether is placed in flask A at the start and the rest added in portions as the magnesium is consumed. The addition of methyl bromide should be stopped just as the magnesium is consumed. After being held at reflux for 10–15 min, the methylmagnesium bromide reagent is ready for the next step.

Reaction of methylmagnesium bromide with 3,3,5-trimethylcyclohexanone

3,3,5-Trimethylcyclohexanone may be obtained from the Hugo Stinnes Chemical Co., 415 Madison Avenue, N.Y., 10017. Before this ketone was available, isophorone (3,3,5-trimethyl-2-cyclohexenone) was used in this experiment [1]. The yield of desired tertiary alcohol is smaller when isophorone is used. However, fractionation of the ether yields 1,3,5,5-tetramethyl-1,3-cyclohexadiene which can be added to that obtained by dehydration of the tertiary alcohol. The factors which affect the nature of the products formed from isophorone and methylmagnesium bromide have been discussed [9].

A solution of 3,3,5-trimethylcyclohexanone in ether is added from the separatory funnel D (Figure 5-1). The rate of addition is determined by noting the rate of reflux at drip tip E. After the addition of the ketone has been completed, a period of reflux is in order.

How should one be able to decide when the reaction is complete? This question should be considered not only for the present reaction but also for reactions involving other Grignard reagents.

The tertiary alcohol produced is in the form of its bromomagnesium salt which is soluble in ether. Two general procedures are available to convert this salt to the free alcohol. In one procedure dilute hydrochloric acid is added slowly while cooling and stirring until two clear layers are produced, an upper ether layer and a lower aqueous one. The ether layer is worked up as described (see page 14). Unless the tertiary alcohol produced is extraordinarily sensitive to acid, this technique is satisfactory. The main disadvantage is that the technique is time consuming on a large scale. The other procedure involves the dropwise addition, with vigorous stirring, of a saturated solution of ammonium chloride. The end point of addition of the ammonium chloride occurs when there is an abrupt change in the nature of the solid and the solution. If the stirring is stopped at this point the ether solution appears clear and not at all hazy. Then pour the ether solution into a flask for removal of solvent. The solids remaining in the reaction flask should be washed with further portions of ether, or ether-benzene, to effect almost quantitative transfer.

Do not discard the solid residue in the flask until the yield has been determined. If the proper point was reached when the ether was poured off there should be only a few percent of tertiary alcohol remaining in the solids.

Solvent can then be removed from the combined extracts. If the tertiary alcohol is desired as the final product, the residue can be vacuum distilled directly. In the present case proceed directly to the dehydration without vacuum distillation.

Dehydration of tertiary alcohol to tetramethylcyclohexenes

The crude tertiary alcohol obtained by either of the procedures just described is placed together with a small amount of potassium acid sulfate in a Claisen flask (see Figure 4-1) fitted to a small un-packed column leading to a water-cooled receiver. On heating, de-hydration will commence at some temperature. This operation is best conducted under reduced pressure so that the water and olefin formed distill and leave the unchanged tertiary alcohol in the flask. The column need be only efficient enough to allow this fractionation to occur. By using this technique, the olefin formed is removed rapidly from the acid catalyst. Since the olefin is relatively low boiling, an efficient condensing system is required. A clean trap should be used in the system so that any olefin trapped can be used.

After the reaction has been completed, the olefin can readily be separated from the water by distillation. Transfer the olefin-water mixture in a small amount of solvent over a cone of magnesium sulfate (see page 18) to a suitable flask, and distill. The overall yield of tetramethylcyclohexenes (position of double bond variable) at this stage should be 70–80%.

In an alternate procedure the tertiary alcohol may be dehydrated by passing in the vapor phase over an alumina catalyst, see reference [1]. The preparation of olefins by vapor-phase pyrolysis of acetates of secondary and primary alcohols is usually markedly superior to batch dehydration of the corresponding alcohols.

Vapor–Phase Aromatization

A suitable apparatus for vapor-phase reactions is illustrated in Figure 5-5. A reactor tube A is held in upright position in an insulated furnace B which is securely placed on a platform attached to the laboratory wall.

A Lindberg Hevi-duty furnace (59544) and pyrometer control is satisfactory. The construction of a home-made furnace is described briefly in L. F. Fieser, Experiments in Organic Chemistry, *Part II, 2nd edition, D. C. Heath and Co., New York, page 383.*

The temperature of B is controlled by a suitable regulating device C. The reactor tube A is packed with a suitable catalyst in the bottom section D (about 20 in.) and with glass beads at the top E (about 6 in.). The material to be pyrolyzed is added through the Hershberg dropping funnel F [10] and the products of reaction (excluding noncondensible gas) are collected in the receiver G which is cooled by the cooling bath H.

If the gas formed is desired, collection over an appropriate liquid can be effected through I.

The tube A is held in place mainly by a clamp at J (which has asbestos paper between the clamp and the tube) but also by the blocks K, L.

The construction of these blocks is shown in the insert in Figure 5-5. The two halves are held together by nuts and bolts as shown. The larger circle M represents a groove which fits the extension of the inner tube N of the furnace B at top and bottom. The inner hole of the clamp K, is conical to fit A. Compare with Figure 4–5.

For the pyrolysis of the tetramethylcyclohexene mixture, the catalyst is prepared essentially as described in reference [1] with one exception. Alumina pellets are placed in a round-bottomed flask and covered with a saturated (about 260 g of $Cr(NO_3)_3 \cdot 9H_2O$ in 600 ml of water) solution of chromic nitrate.

Alumina pellets may be obtained from the Harshaw Chemical Co., Cleveland, Ohio, Al-0104 T 3/10.

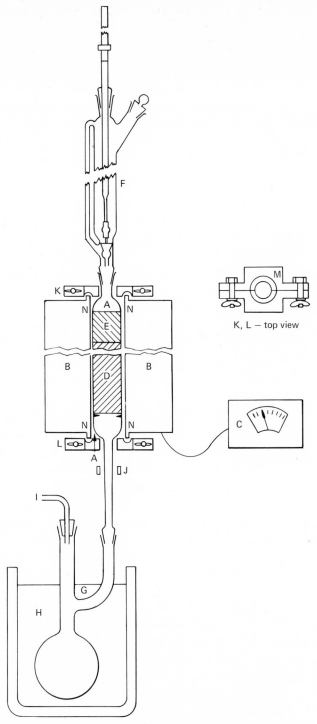

Figure 5-5. Vapor-phase reaction apparatus.

K, L — top view

The flask is evacuated by means of a water pump which causes much of the air entrapped in the alumina pellets to be removed. When bubbling of the pellets ceases, the vacuum is broken and liquid fills the pores. This achieves a more thorough impregnation of the alumina than if a vacuum is not applied. The alumina pellets are then removed, dried overnight in an oven at 110–120°C.

When preparing a catalyst for a single run, the alumina need be treated only once with chromium salts (compare ref. [1]).

The dried pellets are then placed in section D of the reactor tube and topped with glass beads placed in section E. Air is passed through the tube which is heated to about 400°C until the catalyst is dry (overnight is satisfactory). Nitrogen is then passed through for a short time to displace the air and then hydrogen for as long as appreciable water is being formed (1–2 hr). The catalyst bed is now ready for use.

The dropping funnel F, containing the olefin mixture, and the receiver G, surrounded by the dry ice–acetone cooling bath H, are put in place. A tube should be led from the exit tube I to a hood or out of a window.

The exit tube should be in use while the hydrogen is flowing.

The temperature of the reactor tube should now be raised to 480 ± 5°C and the olefin mixture is dripped onto the glass beads in section E at a rate of about 30–45 ml/h. When this step is completed the crude mesitylene should be tested to ascertain if the aromatization has been complete. Testing is conveniently performed by vapor-phase chromatography. Alternatively a small portion of the product is mixed with a few drops of cold, concentrated sulfuric acid in a small test tube. If little coloration develops in the acid layer and the volume of the organic layer remains essentially constant, aromatization has been fairly complete. The main batch can now safely be washed with portions of cold, concentrated sulfuric acid (mesitylene sulfonates readily if the temperature is too high) until the washings are colorless. The mesitylene is then taken up in a small amount of ether. This solution is washed with water and saturated sodium chloride and dried as previously described (see page 17). On distillation pure mesitylene is obtained. Overall yields of 50–75% are generally obtained.

REFERENCES

[1] Ferrin, J. P., T. B. Tom, N. L. Koslin, K. W. Greenlee, J. M. Dexter, and C. E. Boord, *J. Org. Chem.*, **19**, 923 (1954).

[2] Fieser, L. F. and M. Fieser, *Reagents for Organic Synthesis*, John Wiley and Sons, Inc., New York, 1967, p. 105.

[3] Orchin, M., *Ind. Eng. Chem.*, **17**, 99 (1945).

[4] Pearson, D. E., D. Cowan, and J. D. Beckler, *J. Org. Chem.*, **24**, 504 (1959).

[5] See Fieser, L. F., and M. Fieser, *Reagents for Organic Synthesis*, John Wiley and Sons, Inc., New York, 1967, pp. 415–424 for a description of titration of Grignard reagents, other information of interest, and many references. The use of 4-phenylazodiphenylamine as an internal indicator for titration of Grignard reagents has been recommended by Magerlein, B. J., and W. P. Schneider, *J. Org. Chem.*, **34**, 1179 (1969).

[6] See Young, W. G., J. F. Lane, A. Loshokoff, and S. Winstein, *J. Amer. Chem. Soc.*, **59**, 2441 (1937) and references therein.

[7] Newman, M. S., and J. H. Wotiz, *J. Amer. Chem. Soc.*, **71**, 1292 (1949).

[8] Reimschuessel, H. K., *J. Org. Chem.*, **25**, 2256 (1960).

[9] Kharasch, M. S., and P. O. Tawney, *J. Amer. Chem. Soc.*, **63**, 2308 (1941).

[10] Organic Synthesis, Coll. Vol. II, p. 129.

Six

The Synthesis of 1-Keto-1,2,3,4, 5,6,7,8- octahydroanthracene

This experiment comprises a three-step synthetic sequence by which a new six-membered ring is introduced on an aromatic ring.

Step 1. Friedel–Crafts condensation of succinic anhydride and tetralin (1,2,3,4-tetrahydronaphthalene) to yield β-(5,6,7,8-tetrahydro-2-naphthoyl)propionic acid (**I**).

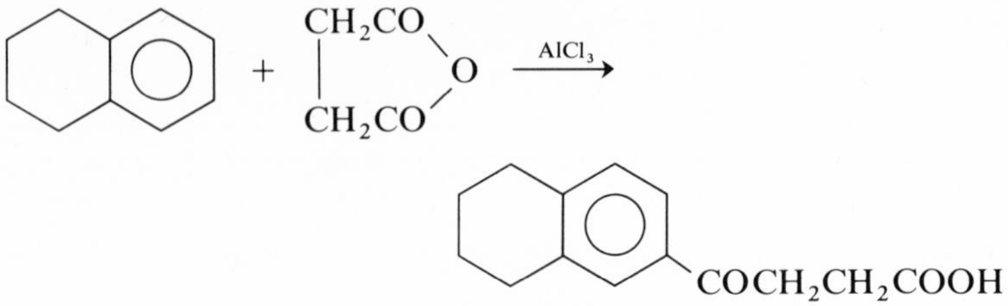

I

Step 2. Reduction of **I** by the Martin–Clemmensen and/or Wolff–Kishner route to γ-(5,6,7,8-tetrahydro-2-naphthyl)butyric acid (**II**).

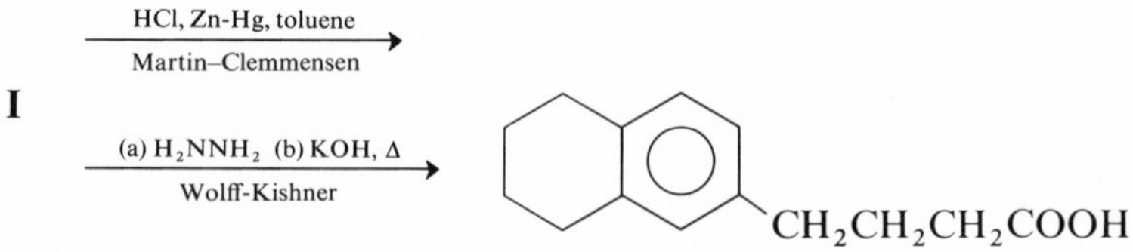

II

Step 3. Cyclization of **II** to 1-keto-1,2,3,4,5,6,7,8-octahydroanthracene (**III**).

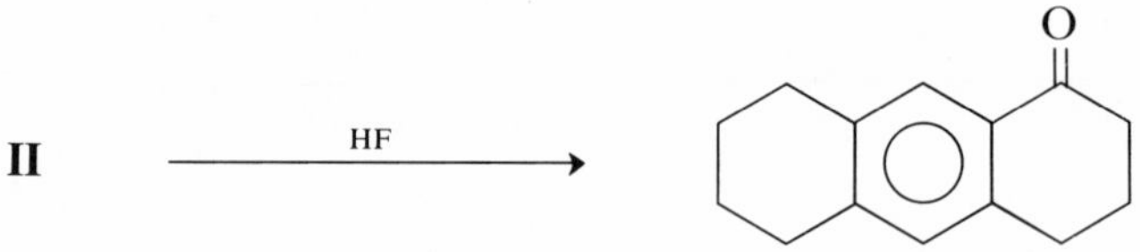

III

The techniques covered include a reaction in which a gas is evolved, a heterogeneous reaction, and a reaction in liquid hydrogen fluoride. In the step 1 the reaction may be run on a 1-mole scale so that experience in handling large amounts of material may be gained.

Friedel-Crafts Acylation

When Friedel–Crafts acylations are carried out on naphthalene, mixtures of 1- and 2-substituted naphthalene derivatives are often obtained. However, acylation of tetralin yields mainly 2-substituted-5,6,7,8-tetrahydronaphthalenes. Hence, if a 2-substituted naphthalene is desired, the route which starts with tetralin and later involves a dehydrogenation step may be preferable to the route which starts with napthalene and requires a separation of isomers.

A description of the formation of a mixture of β-(1-and 2-naphthoyl)-propionic acids and their separation is available [1].

For best results the tetralin used should be peroxide-free.

To test for peroxides a few milliliters of sample should be shaken with acidified potassium iodide solution. A brown-to-violet color indicates that peroxides are present. In this event, the tetralin should be shaken in a separatory funnel several times with cold 70–80% sulfuric acid. The tetralin layer is then washed with water and distilled under reduced pressure. If protected from air and light, purified tetralin remains peroxide-free.

About 1.5 moles of tetralin and 1 mole of succinic anhydride are dissolved in 1 liter of benzene in a 2-liter, three-necked flask A, fitted with a motor driven stirrer B, a reflux condenser C, and a solids-addition flask D connected to A by a length of wide rubber tubing E and supported by the ring F as shown in Figure 6-1.

The feature of the rubber tubing E is advantageous whenever solids are to be added to reaction mixtures. The tubing and D should be removed and replaced with a Ŧ stopper as soon as all of the solid has been added. If the tubing is then washed and dried it will last for a long time.

Many different types of stirrers have been used by organic chemists. The type of stirrer used in Friedel–Crafts reactions is important because there are often marked changes in the viscosity of the reaction system as solid aluminum chloride is added. These changes in viscosity are due to the formation of solid complexes, which dissolve at rates dependent on the solvent used and the temperature maintained. A versatile stirring assembly is shown in Figure 6-1. The shaft B of the stirrer is made of stainless steel. The glass bearing G should fit the steel rod snugly. The length of the bearing depends on the size of the apparatus. It is advisable to have

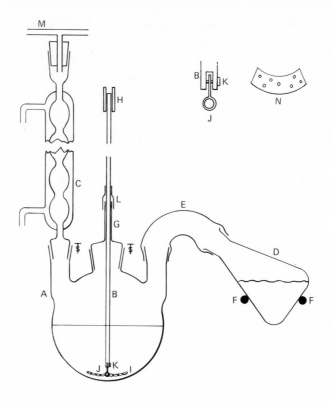

Figure 6-1. Apparatus for Friedel–Crafts acylations.

several sizes affixed to 🍉 joints to go into the center neck of different size reaction flasks. The length of the stirring rod B depends on the size flask to be used. The distance from the stirrer chuck H to the bearing G should be about the same as that from G to the loop J. The bottom of the stirring rod B contains a small hole (see insert, Figure 6-1) into which small metal loops J may be fastened by means of the set screw K. The twisted wire stirrers I attached to the loops J make excellent stirrers [2]. It is advisable to keep several sizes of such stirrers for use with different size flasks and also different length stirring rods.

Alternatively, small curved flat perforated metal stirrers, which swivel on a pin located at the same position as K, can be used. The curve of this type of metal stirrer approximates the curvature of the round-bottomed flask to be used. For a suggested stirrer see insert N, Figure 6-1.

Access of air to the apparatus is prevented by the short length of rubber tubing L which should just touch the shaft and is lubricated at the juncture with glycerine.

This device is more convenient than mercury-sealed devices or "Trubore" shafts. The latter are expensive and require very careful alignment with the shaft of the motor stirrer if serious vibration is to be avoided.

Somewhat more than two equivalents of aluminum chloride are needed to effect condensations of acid anhydrides with aromatic hydrocarbons. The first equivalent converts the anhydride into a dichloroaluminum salt and an acyl chloride. The second equivalent is bound as a complex to the ketone formed on acylation. Evolution of hydrogen chloride indicates the progress of this step, and the excess over two equivalents ensures that the rate of acylation of the last 5–10% is not too slow. The equations below represent the stoichiometry.

$$(RCO)_2O + AlCl_3 \rightarrow RCOCl + RCOOAlCl_2$$
$$RCOCl + ArH + AlCl_3 \rightarrow RCOAr \cdot AlCl_3 + HCl$$

Experience here has shown that high yields of β-(5,6,7,8-tetra-hydro-2-naphthoyl)propionic acid **I** may be obtained with almost any grade of anhydrous aluminum chloride when added judiciously. If the rate of addition from D is too slow and the temperature in the reaction mixture too low, there can be stirring difficulties. The addition of the aluminum chloride should be reasonably rapid and the temperature held below the boiling point of the mixture. The rate of condensation reaction can be conveniently gauged by waving an open bottle of concentrated ammonia near the exit tube *M* at the top of C.

This tube is shown as a T-tube. If the reaction is not carried out in a hood, this tube should be attached to a water aspirator to prevent hydrogen chloride fumes from spreading. Even in a hood this may be desirable to protect the motor stirrer from hydrogen chloride.

The size of the cloud of ammonium chloride produced acts as an indicator. After all of the aluminum chloride has been added, the reaction mixture may be heated to reflux.

Commercial aluminum chloride, Grade No. 1 coarse, obtained from the Solvay Process Division of the Allied Chemical Corp., is preferred to finely divided analytical reagent grade aluminum chloride as control of the rate of reaction is easier. Also, since the yields are just as high, the low cost of crude aluminum chloride is an advantage.

However, long periods of reflux make purification of the product more difficult. The best criterion to use in timing the reflux period is the rate of evolution of hydrogen chloride from M. This evolution never stops but, when the rate becomes slow, the reaction mixture should be cooled to room temperature for workup.

In general the rate of evolution of hydrogen chloride is the best way to judge how to run an acylation. The temperature should be kept from rising as long as the rate of gas evolution is rapid. For example, if gas is evolved rapidly at 30–40°C there is no need to heat to 80–100° for any length of time at the end. One may gain an extra 5% of acylation at the expense of 5% of product undergoing self-condensation. Close observation of the color of the reaction mixture is also important in certain cases, especially those involving ring closure of acyl chlorides. The complexes formed between the acyl chloride and aluminum chloride are generally pale yellow to orange-red. However, the complexes of the cyclic ketones are dark colored. Hence, if the color does not change markedly after the first 20–30% of aluminum chloride has been added, the temperature should be raised until the cyclization

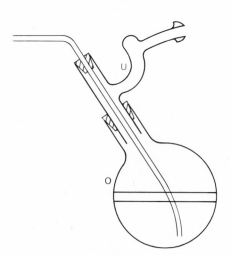

Figure 6-2. Steam distillation flask and adapter.

starts (hydrogen chloride evolution). Further addition of aluminum chloride is then resumed.

The stirrer and reflux condenser are removed and the mixture is poured in several portions, onto crushed ice in a 5-liter round-bottomed flask O (Figure 6-2). The amount of ice is judged by the desirability of having the resulting mixture hot but not boiling when all of the reaction mixture has been quantitatively transferred to O. One equivalent of hydrochloric acid (why?) is added to O, and steam distillation in the apparatus shown in Figure 6-2 is begun.

Steam from a steam line is led into the trap P at Q and out at R (see Figure 6-3). The tube S is useful to allow condensed water in P to be led to a sink by manipulation of a pinch (or screw) clamp T.

By leaving a screw clamp T slightly open, the rate of water removal may be regulated with almost no attention over a lengthy steam distillation. An alternate improved steam trap is described [3].

The Claisen adapter U (Figure 6-2) is useful for preventing non-volatile material from being carried over into the condenser V (Figure 6-4), to which it is connected by means of a ball joint. The copper coil condenser W is much more effective as a condenser than glass devices in common use. A 12-in. long coil of 1/4-in. OD copper

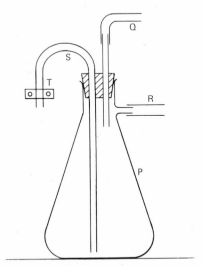

Figure 6-3. Trap for steam distillation.

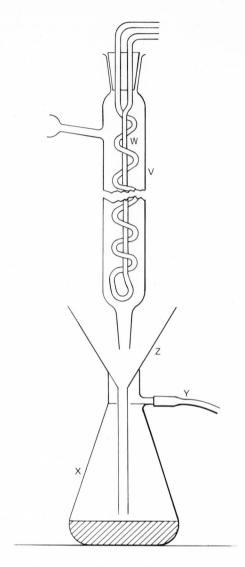

Figure 6-4. Copper coil condenser.

tubing with turns about 3/4 in. apart and about $1\frac{1}{2}$ in. wide is extremely efficient.

If a lengthy steam distillation is involved and the desired product is sufficiently dense that almost none of it floats, the distillate can be collected in a suction flask X arranged so that the overflow at Y goes into a sink (or into a separatory funnel for solvent extraction). The distillate is introduced into X by a long-stemmed funnel Z which ensures that the heavier material will collect at bottom of X. A somewhat more elaborate device is described [4].

Steam distillation of the hydrolyzed reaction mixture is continued until the benzene has been removed. The adapter is removed and the flask O (Figure 6-2) is cooled under running water. As the upper layer of molten acid solidifies, the flask is swirled just enough so that, when solidification is complete, the bottom aqueous layer can be poured off and extracted with benzene.

This benzene extract is then poured back on the organic acid and about 200 ml of dilute hydrochloric acid is added. The mixture is steam distilled for a short while and the cooling procedure repeated. After pouring off the aqueous acid layer and rinsing the remaining solid with several portions of dilute hydrochloric acid, the organic acid fraction is covered with a solution containing a small excess of potassium carbonate. The mixture is then steamed again for a few minutes. If the removal of aluminum salts by the hydrochloric acid treatments has been complete, a clear solution of the potassium salt of I will result.

Potassium salts of organic acids are generally more water soluble than sodium salts. If the potassium salt of an acid is not sufficiently soluble, the diethanolamine salt can be used as it is often much more soluble.

Any insoluble material (mainly aluminum hydroxide) should be removed by filtration through a Buchner funnel. If the solution is darker than pale yellow, decolorization by treatment with decolorizing charcoal is indicated.

Before treating the entire solution with charcoal, a small portion should be tested to see if the treatment will be successful and to estimate the amount of charcoal needed.

The treatment with charcoal is best carried out at room temperature rather than in boiling solvent, as preferential adsorption of material on charcoal is better at lower temperatures. The clear, pale filtrate is now ready for acidification.

Directions in the literature often suggest liberation of an organic acid from its salt by adding a strong acid. However, in practice the addition of the salt solution to excess acid is preferable because the carbon dioxide liberated causes less foaming trouble if the medium is acid.

An additional advantage of adding the organic salt to the acid is that, when the mineral acid is in excess, there is little chance that a very insoluble precipitate (composed of equal amounts of the salt of the acid and the free acid) will be formed. Such a precipitate is quite insoluble in aqueous base and also in organic solvents. If encountered, these complex salts may be solubilized by heating with aqueous-alcoholic potassium hydroxide.

The alkaline solution should be added in portions after allowing time for the first amount of freed acid to crystallize. Subsequent additions of the alkaline solution should be made with continued swirling so that a nicely crystalline acid will result and, hence, an easily filterable slurry will be obtained.

The preciptate is now collected on a Buchner funnel and washed well with water. After drying to constant weight, the crude yield may be calculated (usually over 90%). Pure acid may be obtained by crystallization from a suitable solvent.

If, as in the present case, the acid is to be further reacted, the drying is unnecessary. The moist acid, as obtained by aid of the rubber dam technique (see page 58), may be directly reduced by the Wolff–Kishner or the Martin–Clemmensen method. An estimate of the yield can be obtained by noting the loss in weight on drying a representative sample.

An alternative method of isolation is preferable whenever the organic acid is sufficiently soluble in ether-benzene. The alkaline solution is poured into aqueous acid in a separatory funnel containing sufficient ether-benzene to dissolve the free acid. After the acidification is complete (caution is needed in shaking because of the evolution of carbon dioxide) the organic layer containing the acid is washed with water, then with saturated salt solution, and filtered through a cone of magnesium sulfate as described (see page 18). After distillation of the ether, crystallization can be effected from the benzene remaining or from another solvent system as the case may be. More nearly quantitative isolations may be made more rapidly using this technique. For large quantities of less soluble acids, the precipitation-filtration technique may be preferable.

Clemmensen–Martin Reduction [5]

The reduction of a ketonic carbonyl to a methylene group by means of zinc amalgam and hydrochloric acid is known as the Clemmensen reduction. Yields were often poor before Martin's modification [6], as the reduced product coated the zinc and interfered with reduction. Martin's modification involves two main features: the addition of toluene, in which the reduced product concentrates so that the zinc surface remains clean; and the addition of a small amount of acetic acid, the function of which is uncertain. The type of zinc used for amalgamation plays a role. If granulated zinc is used and stirring is maintained, the reduction time may be greatly reduced [7].

In the case of many heterogeneous reactions, the nature of the solid involved often is an important variable. In general, the duplication of results involving heterogeneous conditions is difficult, and the results are likely to be erratic, even after experience has been gained. Problems often arise in attempts to scale up such reactions. The yield of desired product may drop markedly on quadrupling the size of the run. **Hence, with valuable materials it is often better to make a number of small-scale runs and combine them for workup, rather than to hazard a large-scale run.** Some of the work that has been done on the nature of the zinc used in Clemmensen [7] and Reformatsky [7, 8] reactions has been summarized.

It is of interest in running a Clemmensen–Martin reduction on β-(5,6,7,8-tetrahydro-2-naphthoyl)propionic acid (**I**) to study the effect of variables on the yield of the various products formed (see below). A group discussion is suggested so that agreement can be reached among the workers as to what each will do.

The Clemmensen–Martin reduction is carried out in a one-necked ℑ round-bottomed flask equipped with an efficient reflux condenser essentially as described [6]. Mossy zinc is amalgamated in the reaction flask just before use. The reaction mixture containing **I**, hydrochloric acid, acetic acid, and toluene should be refluxed as rapidly as allowed by the reflux condenser. Additions of concentrated hydrochloric acid can be made through the top of the condenser as needed. In the reduction of **I** periods of 36 to 48 hours are recommended. An interesting variable for study might be the amount of acetic acid added [6].

When a stirred Clemmensen [7] is carried out, granular zinc is used. A three-necked flask setup similar to that illustrated in Figure 6-1 is satisfactory, except that the solids addition flask D is replaced by a small ℑ dropping funnel. The total reduction time (another variable suitable for study) is much less than that required in the Martin modification [6].

After the reduction has been carried out by either method, the reaction mixture is poured into a separatory funnel and separated into acid and neutral fractions by the usual method (see pages 14–19). If all zinc salts are not removed in the washing of the toluene layer with hydrochloric acid, discoloration will result if vacuum distillation is used to purify the γ-(5,6,7,8-tetrahydro-2-naphthyl)butyric acid (**II**). The main acid fraction can be purified by vacuum distillation. Since **II** melts at about 48°C[9], a solids receiver (see page 36) should be used for the vacuum distillation. The yield is usually at least 90%.

Two lactones can usually be isolated by suitable workup of the neutral fraction: the γ-lactone, resulting from ring closure of the hydroxyacid formed by reduction of the ketonic group to a secondary alcohol; and the bis-γ-lactone, resulting from pinacolic reduction. Should one or two bis-γ-lactones be formed?

Wolff–Kishner (W–K) Reduction [10]

Formation of hydrazone. In order to reduce a ketonic function to the corresponding methylene group by the W–K method, the hydrazone must first be made by treating the ketone with excess hydrazine in a suitable solvent. Excess hydrazine is desirable for two reasons: in order to drive the equilibrium shown in equation (6.1) to completion; and to minimize the formation of the azine shown in equation (6.2).

$$\begin{matrix} R \\ \diagdown \\ \diagup \\ R' \end{matrix}\!\!CO + H_2NNH_2 \rightleftharpoons \begin{matrix} R \\ \diagdown \\ \diagup \\ R' \end{matrix}\!\!C{=}NNH_2 + H_2O \qquad 6.1$$

$$\begin{matrix} R \\ \diagdown \\ \diagup \\ R' \end{matrix}\!\!C{=}NNH_2 + \begin{matrix} R \\ \diagdown \\ \diagup \\ R' \end{matrix}\!\!CO \rightleftharpoons \begin{matrix} R \\ \diagdown \\ \diagup \\ R' \end{matrix}\!\!C{=}NN{=}C\!\!\begin{matrix} R \\ \diagup \\ \diagdown \\ R' \end{matrix} + H_2O \qquad 6.2$$

In many cases where poor yields of reduction product are obtained, the fault lies not in the conversion of the hydrazone to the methylene compound but in the poor yield of hydrazone obtained. Hence, tests should be made to ensure that hydrazone formation has been effected in high yield before proceeding.

After hydrazone formation has been completed, the water and excess hydrazine must be removed so that the higher temperatures needed for completion of the subsequent steps (see equations 6.3–6.7) may be attained. Hence, if the W–K reduction is carried out in diethylene glycol, b.p. 245°C, the hydrazone need not be isolated. Distillation results in a forerun of water and hydrazine. The temperature then climbs to the desired point (see page 138).

Conversion of hydrazone to product. The reactions involved in conversion of the hydrazone to product are summarized below.

$$\underset{R'}{\overset{R}{\diagdown}}C{=}NNH_2 + B^- \rightleftharpoons \underset{R'}{\overset{R}{\diagdown}}C{=}NNH^- \leftrightarrow$$

$$\underset{R'}{\overset{R}{\diagdown}}\overset{-}{C}{-}N{=}NH + BH \qquad \textbf{6.3}$$

$$\underset{R'}{\overset{R}{\diagdown}}\overset{-}{C}{-}N{=}NH + BH \rightleftharpoons \underset{R'}{\overset{R}{\diagdown}}CH{-}N{=}NH + B^- \qquad \textbf{6.4}$$

$$\underset{R'}{\overset{R}{\diagdown}}CH{-}N{=}NH + B^- \rightleftharpoons \underset{R'}{\overset{R}{\diagdown}}CHN{=}N^- + BH \qquad \textbf{6.5}$$

$$\underset{R'}{\overset{R}{\diagdown}}CHN{=}N^- \rightarrow \underset{R'}{\overset{R}{\diagdown}}CH^- + N_2 \qquad \textbf{6.6}$$

$$\underset{R'}{\overset{R}{\diagdown}}CH^- + BH \rightarrow \underset{R'}{\overset{R}{\diagdown}}CH_2 + B^- \qquad \textbf{6.7}$$

Various bases have been used in the W–K reduction [7]. As illustrated by equations (6.3) through (6.7), the reactions require a strong base which is not used up in the reaction. Hence the quantity of base generally recommended is probably greater than necessary. In general, the stronger the base used the shorter the time and the lower the temperature required for completion of the reaction.

In most cases, including the present experiment, a solution of potassium hydroxide is involved at the start. As distillation of water and hydrazine (see below) is effected, the concentration of water in the reaction mixture decreases so that the effective base is the conjugate base of the solvent, diethylene glycol.

The evolution of nitrogen provides a built-in indicator for the temperature at which the reaction should be carried out and the length of time for heating. The temperature is raised until the rate of evolution of nitrogen is fairly rapid, and the reaction is allowed to proceed until nitrogen evolution ceases. Since hot solutions of potassium hydroxide etch glass flasks badly, W–K reductions of this type are better carried out in stainless steel flasks.

Because holes may be formed during a run, the use of glass flasks is ill advised.

As these are not generally available in different sizes the flasks illustrated in Figure 6-5 are recommended.

Simpler round-bottomed stainless steel flasks with 24/40 ⑂ joints can be used, except that the temperature at which nitrogen evolution is occurring is unknown.

The ketone to be reduced (in this experiment the ketoacid **I**) is put into the metal flask A together with potassium hydroxide, hydrazine (usually 85% hydrazine is satisfactory), and diethylene glycol (triethylene glycol has also been used).

In different cases varying ratios of reactants are recommended in the literature. After thought and discussion, the student should decide what ratio is satisfactory. Several students may wish to cooperate and try out the effect of changing the ratio of reactants.

The mixture is heated (a hot plate or suitably designed heating mantle) to reflux until hydrazone formation is complete. In most cases heating for 1–2 hr is sufficient. The removal of water and excess hydrazine is easily regulated through the slanting-bore stopcock B of the Hershberg (see page 20) distilling-reflux condenser C.

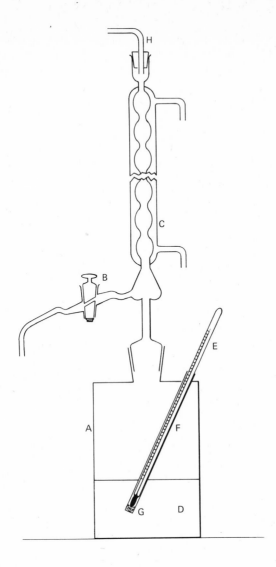

Figure 6-5. Metal flask for Wolff–Kishner reductions.

After most of the water and hydrazine have been removed, the temperature of the reaction mixture D begins to rise as noted on thermometer E in the thermometer well F (containing glass wool G to avoid breakage of thermometers). Material is allowed to distill until the evolution of gas becomes rapid. The evolution of gas can be noted by attaching to exit tube H a tube leading to an inverted graduate filled with water. Stopcock B is then closed and the mixture heated until gas evolution ceases. In most cases only 30–50 min are needed.

In many cases reported in the literature, the reactions are run at temperatures considerably higher than necessary and for much longer times than needed. Undoubtedly, measurement of the nitrogen produced was not used as an indicator of the progress of the reaction.

If less than the theoretical amount of nitrogen is collected, longer heating is of no avail because hydrazone formation was incomplete (or there was a leak). The reaction mixture is then cooled and transferred quantitatively to a separatory funnel for workup.

If the reaction mixture is not worked up as soon as heating is discontinued, the distilling reflux condenser must be removed before allowing the metal flask to cool to room temperature. If this precaution is not taken, the standard taper glass joint will prove difficult to remove from the neck of the metal flask. The reason is that the metal neck contracts and holds the glass joint firmly.

The yield of material suitable for the next step should be above 90%. Vacuum distillation is preferable to recrystallization for the purification of the crude acid.

Cyclization in anhydrous hydrogen fluoride [11]

Liquid hydrogen fluoride can cause burns which may not be felt immediately. If a drop of hydrogen fluoride may have splashed on your skin, rinse the affected part well with water and apply a paste of magnesia, water, and glycerine. This paste should be made up in advance and kept in the hood in which the reaction is carried out.

For the cyclization of γ-(5,6,7,8-tetrahydro-2-naphthyl)butyric acid (**II**) to 1-keto-1,2,3,4,5,6,7,8-octahydroanthracene (**III**), anhydrous hydrogen fluoride is quite useful. A quantity of **II** (5–10 g) is placed in a small polyethylene bottle A and anhydrous hydrogen fluoride is added (about 10 ml/g of **II**). The anhydrous hydrogen fluoride has been obtained by condensing hydrogen fluoride from a pressure cylinder in a dry ice–acetone cooled copper coil condenser B as shown in Figure 6-6.

This operation should be carried out in a good hood. The inside of the glass windows of the hood should be protected by covering

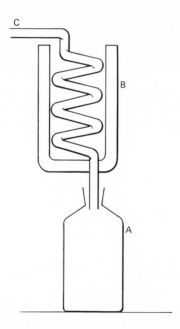

Figure 6-6. Copper coil condenser for hydrogen fluoride.

with polyethylene film. It is advisable to reserve one hood for these hydrogen fluoride reactions as corrosion of metal fixtures occurs in addition to etching of all glass in the vicinity. When handling containers which have liquid hydrogen fluoride in them, rubber gloves should be worn. The condenser B should be firmly supported so that the polyethylene receiver A which is to be the reaction vessel can easily be clamped in place. The top of the copper coil C should be connected to the tube E (Figure 6-7) of the hydrogen fluoride cylinder by suitable couplings.

After use, the connections should be separated and immediately cleaned to reduce corrosion. The length of copper tubing leading from the hydrogen fluoride cylinder should not have any bends which allow retention of liquid. The tube E should be long and flexible enough that connection with the coil condenser C (Figure 6-6) can easily be made through a suitable coupling. Although metal couplings have been used here, a Teflon tube of the proper size to fit the copper tubing is preferable.

For opening the valve at the top of the cylinder of hydrogen fluoride, *use two wrenches, as shown in Figure 6-7, which can be turned against each other if properly positioned.* The rectagonal nut D

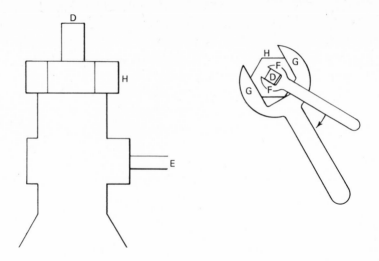

Figure 6-7. Opening of valve of hydrogen fluoride cylinder.

must be turned to open an internal valve in the hydrogen fluoride cylinder so that hydrogen fluoride can come out of tube E. One wrench F is tightened on D and another wrench G is tightened on the hexagonal nut H as shown. By applying pressure on F and G with one hand, valve stem D can be carefully opened without danger of upsetting the hydrogen fluoride cylinder. The degree of turning of D is also easily regulated. By changing the positions of the two wrenches the valve can be closed in a similar way.

After the hydrogen fluoride has been delivered to the polyethylene bottle (which should be marked on the exterior to indicate volume) the contents should be stirred with a metal spatula (rubber gloves) to ensure that solution is complete. The container is placed in a corner near the rear of the hood and allowed to stand overnight. Most of the hydrogen fluoride will have evaporated after this period. Warming will cause most the remaining hydrogen fluoride to evaporate. After adding a solution of potassium carbonate, the reaction mixture is separated into acidic (recovered **II**) and neutral components. Pure **III** is obtained on vacuum distillation. A minimum of 95 % of products (**II** and **III**) should be obtained.

Other Methods for Cyclization of Arylalkanoic Acids

Ring closure of arylalkanoic acids may be accomplished by heating with polyphosphoric acid (PPA) or by conversion to the acid chloride followed by an intramolecular Friedel–Crafts reaction.

In the polyphosphoric acid method, the acid to be cyclized is dissolved in warm polyphosphoric acid. The solution is heated and then poured into water. The temperature required and length of the heating period must be determined for each case [12]. Because of the high viscosity of polyphosphoric acid, the use of methanesulfonic acid as diluent is of advantage. Anhydrous methanesulfonic acid can be prepared by vacuum distillation of commercial material (about 70%).

Ring closure by intramolecular Friedel–Crafts reaction is often the preferred method because of increased yield and ease of laboratory manipulation. The use of phosphorus pentachloride is often preferable to thionyl chloride, as the yield of acyl chloride is higher (see page 38). Furthermore, the use of crude acyl chloride containing the phosphorus oxychloride formed often results in higher yields of ketone than when the acyl chloride is isolated and purified.

Both aluminum chloride and stannic chloride are satisfactory reagents for the cyclization steps. Slightly more than one equivalent is added to a solution of the acyl chloride in benzene or chlorobenzene. Ring closure occurs rapidly at room temperature (or below) and is indicated by evolution of hydrogen chloride and by a marked deepening of color of the reaction mixture. When stannic chloride is used, the rate of ring closure is often greater than in the case of aluminum chloride. Also, the yields are more sensitive to the time allowed for reaction. If the rate of ring closure with stannic chloride is very rapid, the reaction can often be moderated by removing the phosphorus oxychloride by vacuum distillation before the treatment with stannic chloride. In general yields of cyclized products are greater when the reactions are not allowed to run for an appreciable time after the brisk evolution of hydrogen chloride has occurred. It is better to err on the short side because, on workup, uncyclized acid can be recovered by an alkaline extraction (after acid washings remove aluminum or tin salts). If the reaction is allowed to go on for too long, resinous products are obtained in addition to desired ketone.

REFERENCES

[1] Newman, M. S., R. B. Taylor, T. Hodgson, and A. B. Garrett, *J. Amer. Chem. Soc.*, **69**, 1784 (1947).
[2] Hershberg, E. B., *Ind. Anal. Chem.*, **8**, 313 (1936). See also, Fieser, L. F., *Experiments in Organic Chemistry*, Part II, D. C. Heath and Co., New York, 1941, p. 308.

[3] Tucker, S. H., *Chem. Ind.*, 292 (1953); 194 (1942).

[4] Wallenberger, F. T., W. F. O'Connor, and E. J. Moriconi, *J. Chem. Educ.*, **36**, 251 (1959).

[5] Martin, E. L., *Organic Reactions*, John Wiley and Sons, Inc., New York, 1957, chap. 7.

[6] Martin, E. L., *J. Amer. Chem. Soc.*, **58**, 1438 (1936).

[7] Fieser, L. F., and M. Fieser, *Reagents for Organic Synthesis*, John Wiley and Sons, Inc., New York, 1967, pp. 1287–1289.

[8] Natelson, S., and S. P. Gottfried, *J. Amer. Chem. Soc.*, **61**, 970 (1939).

[9] Newman, M. S., and H. V. Zahm, *J. Amer. Chem. Soc.*, **65**, 1097 (1943).

[10] See Fieser, L. F., and M. Fieser, *Reagents for Organic Synthesis*, John Wiley and Sons, Inc., New York, 1967, pp. 435–438. See also Cram, D. J., M. R. V. Sahyun, and G. R. Knox, *J. Amer. Chem. Soc.*, **84**, 1734 (1962).

[11] See reference 7, p. 455.

[12] See Fieser, L. F., and M. Fieser, *Reagents for Organic Synthesis*, John Wiley and Sons, Inc., New York, 1967, p. 894, for a number of examples which involve polyphosphoric acid.

Seven

The Synthesis of
1-Heptyne

The object of this experiment is to prepare 1-heptyne by the reaction of monosodium acetylide with *n*-amyl bromide in liquid ammonia.

$$HC\equiv CNa + CH_3(CH_2)_3CH_2Br \rightarrow HC\equiv C(CH_2)_4CH_3 + NaBr$$

The technique involved illustrates running reactions in liquid ammonia [1]. Liquid ammonia is in some respects a unique solvent for carrying out reactions in organic chemistry. It has a high dielectric constant (26.7 at $-60°C$) in comparison with most common organic solvents yet is a reasonably good solvent for many organic compounds. Furthermore, reactions involving stronger bases than can exist in water or alcoholic solvents can be carried out in ammonia [2, 3].

Ammonia has a low boiling point ($-33°C$) and a relatively high heat of vaporization (5581 cal/mole); therefore, an efficient reflux condenser is needed to allow reactions in ammonia to be carried out in reasonably short periods of time when reactants on a moderately large scale (1 mole and upwards) are involved. The condenser shown in Figure 7-1 is highly recommended.

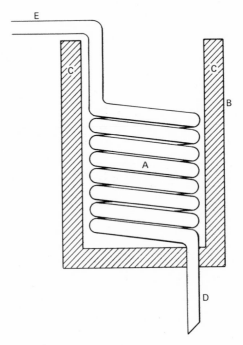

Figure 7-1. Condenser for liquid ammonia reactions.

For small runs a condenser is not needed. See reference [1], pages 192–193.

The condenser A is made of 1/2-in. stainless steel tubing bent into seven helical coils of about $3\frac{3}{4}$-in. outside diameter.

Aluminum tubing has also been used.

The condenser is mounted in a double-walled container B filled with exploded mica C. During a run a dry ice–isopropyl alcohol mixture is used as coolant. The lower end D of the condenser should be fitted by a neoprene stopper to one neck of a suitable three-necked round-bottomed reaction flask fitted with a stirrer as shown in Figure 7-2.

The use of Trubore stirrers K (stirrers with shaft and bearing ground to fit) is recommended here, as plastic stirring blades L are very effective even when the rate of stirring is slow.

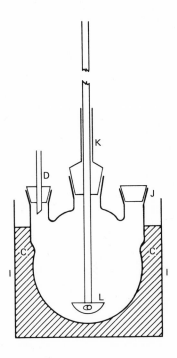

Figure 7-2. Reaction flask for liquid ammonia reactions.

The Synthesis of 1-Heptyne

The upper end E (Figure 7-1) of the condenser should have an adapter for connecting to the bubbler trap shown in Figure 7-3 via tube F so that evolution of gas during a run can be observed. The connection between the long inner tubes G and the symmetrical arrangement ensures that liquid cannot be blown out of the tubes F or sucked back into the reaction vessel. Mineral oil H is a suitable liquid. The two bottles may be taped together for convenience in handling.

The reaction flask (Figure 7-2) is supported in a bed of exploded mica C held in a paper-board box I. It should be possible to lower I away from the flask at the end of the reaction. The level of the mica is adjusted so that the nature of the reaction mixture can be observed at different stages. A wash bottle containing alcohol is helpful in removing the frost, which collects at all uninsulated positions of the reaction flask, whenever the interior of the flask or the drip tip of the reflux condenser must be seen to observe the rate of reflux.

Ammonia can be condensed so rapidly with the condenser illustrated in Figure 7-1 that it returns in a continuous stream. Isopropyl alcohol is preferable to acetone in the coolant mixture as there is less foaming when the condensation rate of ammonia is high. The quantity of isopropyl alcohol used in a condenser must be determined by experiment. If too much is used, foaming over the top of the condenser is a problem. If too little is used, the condenser will not operate at peak efficiency.

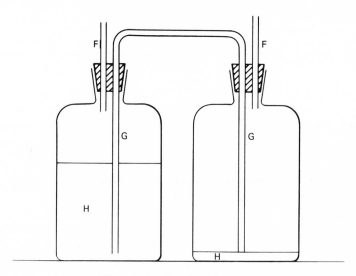

Figure 7-3. Gas bubbler trap.

Liquid ammonia is introduced into the neck J (Figure 7-2) by a Tygon tube connected to a cylinder of liquid ammonia which has been laid on the floor and tilted toward the valve end. In this position the pressure forces liquid ammonia through the connecting tube into the flask through J when the release valve is opened. A heavy outside crayon mark on the flask is helpful to indicate when the desired amount of ammonia has been introduced. In this experiment 400 ml is ample for a 1-mole run.

After the ammonia has been collected, the preparation of sodium acetylide is carried out. The following equations are of interest.

$$2\,Na + 4\,NH_3 \rightarrow 2\,Na^+ + 2e(NH_3)_2 \qquad \textbf{7.1}$$

$$2\,e(NH_3)_2 \xrightarrow[\text{Fe}]{\text{cat.}} H_2 + 2\,NH_2^- + 2NH_3 \qquad \textbf{7.2}$$

$$(\text{overall})\ 2\,Na + 2\,NH_3 \rightarrow 2\,NaNH_2 + H_2 \qquad \textbf{7.3}$$

$$HC\equiv CH + 2\,NaNH_2 \rightleftharpoons NaC\equiv CNa + 2\,NH_3 \qquad \textbf{7.4}$$

$$NaC\equiv CNa + HC\equiv CH \rightleftharpoons 2\,HC\equiv CNa \qquad \textbf{7.5}$$

Sodium (also other metals) dissolves rapidly in liquid ammonia to give blue solutions (equation 7.1) which are powerful reducing agents. The color of these solutions has been ascribed to solvated electrons. No hydrogen is evolved from these solutions even when maintained for long periods of time.

If the ammonia used is not dry, the blue color will not appear at first. When more than sufficient sodium has been added to react with the water present, the blue color will appear and you can proceed. In some types of reactions, reproducible results are only obtained when pure dry ammonia is used as solvent. Whenever such ammonia is necessary, the amount of ammonia needed is transferred into a flask as described and sufficient sodium to impart a permanent blue color is added. The ammonia is then distilled into a reaction flask shown in Figure 7-2 where condensation is effected by means of condenser A. Such distillation also insures against traces of metallic impurities which may be introduced by using undistilled ammonia.

If, as in the present case, sodium amide is desired (equation 7.2), a small amount (about 0.25 g/mole) of ferric nitrate nonahydrate (more reliable than ferric chloride) is added to the liquid ammonia in which a few grams of sodium has been dissolved. A stream of dry air is then blown through the liquid fairly rapidly by means of a glass tube inserted through J (Figure 7-2). About 20 seconds of aeration are necessary before the blue color has disappeared [4]. The solid neoprene stopper is then replaced at J and a tube is attached at the end of the condenser E (Figure 7-1) which leads to the gas bubbler trap (Figure 7-3) for observing gas evolution. If the iron catalyst has been properly formed, there should be brisk evolution of hydrogen in accordance with equation (7.2). As soon as the hydrogen evolution almost ceases, a further addition of sodium (2–5 g) can be made through J. These additions of sodium are continued until the required amount of sodium has been added. The mixture at the end is quite dark in appearance because of the finely divided iron. Sodium amide is soluble in ammonia to the extent of about 1 g/liter, and, if stirring is stopped, it will settle as a sand-like solid.

The sodium should be washed free of mineral oil with benzene and cut while wet into pieces which will fit easily through neck J. The cut up sodium may be kept under benzene in a covered beaker. When cutting sodium for use in a reaction, always operate in an uncrowded space which is clean, dry, and free of any small objects. A bucket containing dry sand should be at hand to extinguish any fire that may start. *The cutting of sodium is not a dangerous operation if common sense is used. Small pieces of unused sodium should be stored in a bottle under mineral oil for later disposal.*

The reaction represented by equation (7.2) is quite exothermic. If relatively large amounts of sodium amide are to be prepared for isolation and further use as a solid, an ample supply of dry ice is needed for the condenser. After completion of the preparation, the condenser is removed and the paper-board box containing the insulation is lowered from the flask. The ammonia evaporates overnight and the sand-like sodium amide which has a gray cast (due to the iron) can be loosened by stirring with a wooden stick. It is then poured into wide-mouth bottles of colorless glass and the stoppers covered with molten paraffin. Colorless glass is preferable to amber glass because, if it deteriorates due to a leak, sodium amide becomes dangerous and should be disposed of. The danger signal is a yellow color on the surface of the sodium amide—*hence the colorless glass bottle.*

The next step involves the preparation of sodium acetylide by passing acetylene into the stirred suspension of sodium amide (equations 7.4 and 7.5). Acetylene is obtained from cylinders in which it is pressurized in acetone. In order to remove the acetone, the acetylene is passed through a wash bottle containing concentrated sulfuric acid and a drying tower filled with potassium hydroxide pellets. The tube through which acetylene is introduced through J (Figure 7-2) should not dip under the surface of the ammonia because clogging may occur. *A safety T-tube trap (see page 113) should be inserted between the washing train and J.*

As acetylene is passed in, the disodium salt of acetylene is formed (equation 7.4). Because it is relatively insoluble, the mixture assumes a milky appearance. As more acetylene is passed in, the disodium salt is converted to monosodium acetylide (equation 7.5) which is soluble. Hence the milkiness decreases and the solution clears and becomes dark again. Acetylene should be passed in until the solution is saturated with acetylene (rate of addition as observed in the sulfuric acid wash bottle is about the same as gas evolution as measured by the bubbler trap (Figure 7-3) attached at E (Figure 7-1). Because the reaction of acetylene with the bases present is quite exothermic, the rate of addition of acetylene is governed mainly by the efficiency of the reflux condenser.

Sodium acetylide is soluble in ammonia to the extent of 4 mole/liter.

In large runs an ample supply of dry ice is needed.

After the acetylene addition has been completed, the addition of *n*-amyl bromide by means of a pressure-equalizing dropping funnel (see page 109) is started. For a 1-mole run the addition can safely be made in 10–15 min. If other bromides are used the rate of addition can be regulated by noting the change in rate of reflux of ammonia due to the heat of reaction.

The reaction mixture is allowed to stir for about 5 hr to ensure complete reaction of the bromide. It is advisable to keep the reaction mixture saturated with acetylene during the reaction because of its effect on the equilibrium shown in equation (7.7).

$$HC\equiv CNa + C_5H_{11}Br \rightarrow HC\equiv CC_5H_{11} + NaBr \qquad 7.6$$

$$C_5H_{11}C\equiv CH + HC\equiv CNa \rightleftharpoons C_5H_{11}C\equiv CNa + HC\equiv CH \qquad 7.7$$

$$C_5H_{11}C\equiv CNa + C_5H_{11}Br \rightarrow C_5H_{11}C\equiv CC_5H_{11} + NaBr \qquad 7.8$$

The formation of disubstituted acetylenes by the sequence of reactions shown above results in lowering the yield of desired 1-heptyne, but in the present case the loss is not serious.

After the reaction has been completed there are different procedures for working up the product. If the reflux condenser is removed and the box containing the insulation lowered from the flask, ammonia will evaporate. Since 1-heptyne boils at about 100°C the loss of product will not be severe if most of the ammonia is allowed to distill. At some stage water is added to the remaining reaction mixture and the organic layer is separated, washed with dilute hydrochloric acid and saturated salt solution, filtered through a small cone of magnesium sulfate, and distilled.

Alternatively, the solids remaining after evaporation of the ammonia are extracted with ether. The ether layer is washed with dilute acid and saturated salt solution. After filtration through anhydrous magnesium sulfate, the ether is removed by fractional distillation through a helices-packed column with total reflux head. If the ether is distilled without fractionation, there will be some loss of heptyne in the distilled ether.

A column similar to that shown in Figure 4-4, page 86, is useful for distillation at atmospheric pressure. The column is narrower, about 1 in., and it is packed with single turn 3/16-in. helices.

A vapor-phase chromatographic analysis of the crude product before distillation will give an estimate of how much unchanged amyl bromide and 6-dodecyne are present in addition to 1-heptyne. Yields of 70–80% of 1-heptyne are to be expected. Small amounts of 6-dodecyne formed by disproportionation (equation 7.8) are also present.

REFERENCES

[1] Many illustrations of reactions involving acetylene which may be carried out in liquid ammonia are given in Raphael, R. A., *Acetylenic Compounds in Organic Synthesis*, Butterworths Scientific Publications, London, 1955.

[2] Sisler, H. H., *Chemistry in Non-aqueous Solvents*, Reinhold Publishing Corp., New York, 1961, chap. 2.

[3] Watt, G., *Chem. Rev.*, **45**(2), 289–379 (1950).

[4] See Greenlee, K. W., and A. L. Henne, *Inorg. Syn.*, **2**, 128 (1946) for a more detailed description of the preparation of sodium amide.

Eight

Superheated Steam Distillation

Two experiments, each of which involves the technique of super-heated steam distillation, are described in this chapter: I, the synthesis of 4-trichloromethyl-2,4,5-trimethyl-2,5-cyclohexadienone; and II, the synthesis of 1-naphthonitrile.

I. Synthesis of 4-Trichloromethyl-2,4,5-trimethyl-2,5-cyclohexadienone

The objective of this experiment is to convert 2,4,5-trimethyl-phenol into 4-trichloromethyl-2,4,5-trimethyl-2,5-cyclohexadienone. The technique involved is superheated steam distillation.

The condensation of carbon tetrachloride with 4-methylphenols effected by heating with aluminum chloride is known as the Zincke–Suhl reaction [1]. This reaction is of interest because an aromatic compound is converted into a compound in which the aromatic system has been destroyed. The chemistry of the dienones is quite varied as the trichloromethyl group undergoes a variety of 1:3- and 1:5-rearrangement reactions [2]. The product formed from 2,4,5-trimethylphenol in this experiment, in 70–78 % yield, is 4-trichloromethyl-2,4,5-trimethyl-2,5-cyclohexadienone, **I** [3].

Carbon tetrachloride serves both as a reactant and solvent in this reaction. When aluminum chloride (Ohio Apex Division, Food Machinery and Chemical Corporation product) is added, 2,4,5-trichlorophenol reacts to yield the dichloroaluminum salt and hydrogen chloride (equation 8.1). In the next step (equation 8.2), the dichloroaluminum salt formed reacts with carbon tetrachloride to yield the dienone and aluminum chloride; these form a dark-colored complex. Hence, the progress of the condensation reaction cannot be judged by hydrogen chloride evolution, as is usually the case in Friedel–Crafts reactions (see page 129).

Since different grades of aluminum chloride give slightly different results in any particular example of the Zincke–Suhl reaction and the optimum conditions as regards temperature and time of reaction

(2,4,5-trimethylphenol) + AlCl$_3$ $\rightarrow$ (aryl–OAlCl$_2$) + HCl

8.1

(aryl–OAlCl$_2$) + CCl$_4$ $\rightarrow$ (cyclohexadienone–CCl$_3$ derivative, O·AlCl$_3$)

8.2

vary from one phenolic precursor to another [2, 4], the choice of conditions can only be specified after a number of runs has been made in any particular case. In the case of the reaction involving 2,4,5-trimethylphenol, experience at Ohio State has shown that good results are obtained when the reaction is carried out with 0.2 mole of the phenol in 60 ml of carbon tetrachloride at room temperature for 4–5 hr. About two equivalents of aluminum chloride should be used in apparatus similar to that illustrated in Figure 6-1 (see page 128).

After the reaction has been completed, the reaction mixture is poured on ice and hydrochloride acid. The carbon tetrachloride layer is separated from the aqueous layer in a separatory funnel, and the aqueous layer is extracted again with carbon tetrachloride. The combined extracts are placed in a round-bottomed flask A suitable for carrying out superheated steam distillation as shown in Figure 8-1.

Flask A is fitted with an adapter B which has ball C and socket D joints (size 18/9), an inner tube E which fits nearly to the bottom of flask A, and a thermometer well F. The socket joint D fits the metal ball joint G of a stainless steel steam preheater H.

It is convenient to have adapters having the same dimensions between the ball and socket joints, C and D, and inner tubes E fitting 250, 500, 1000, and 2000 ml round-bottomed flasks A. The metal joint G may be replaced by a metal-to-glass seal to a glass ball joint.

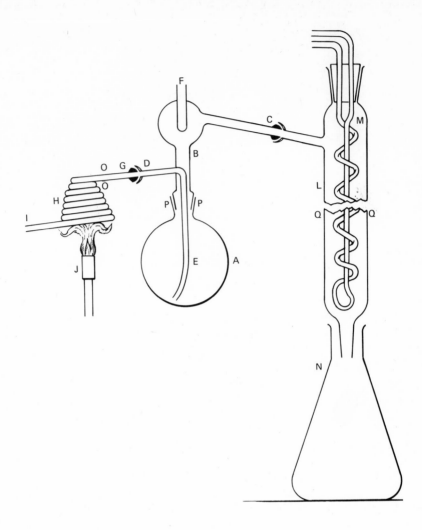

Figure 8-1. Apparatus for superheated steam distillation.

The temperature of the steam emerging from G is controlled by the rate at which steam is delivered into the preheater at I and the amount of heat supplied by the gas burner J. Steam temperature is read on the thermometer placed in the thermometer well F. The vapor emerging from C is condensed in condenser L. The condensing surface is a coiled copper tube M, consisting of approximately 8 ft of 1/4-in. copper tubing.

Metal condensers are much more effective in condensing hot vapors than are glass devices because of the much greater heat conductivity of metal compared with glass. Condenser W, Figure 6-4, is satisfactory (see page 132).

The apparatus is held together by suitable clamps at O, P, and Q. The distillate is collected in receiver N.

It is advisable to have a trap, as shown in Figure 6-3 (see page 131), in the system before the steam enters at H in order that water mixed with the steam and formed by condensation on the walls of the trap can be vented without interruption of the distillation.

The carbon tetrachloride is rapidly steam distilled with mild superheating (steam temperature at 130–140°C) and collected in a separate receiver.

At the start, the rate of addition of steam should be slow in order that the contents of the flask be not splashed up into the adapter B.

As soon as the carbon tetrachloride has been removed, the flame in burner J is increased so that the temperature of the steam is in the 210–230°C range. The steam distillation is continued until all volatile material has been distilled.

It is desirable to have a pair of asbestos gloves at hand so that the hot appratus may be handled at will. It is frequently helpful to be able to twist the flask A during the superheated steam distillation.

This point is easily recognized by observation of the contents of flask A, because only a very small residue should remain therein. No more than 40 min is needed to complete the distillation (the total distillate is not more than 2 liters).

In contrast, superheated steam distillation of a similar compound at 130°C required about 43 liters of distillate for a comparably sized run [5]. The temperature of the superheated steam is important in cutting down the time needed for completion of the distillation. The higher the temperature, the shorter the time and the smaller the total volume of distillate.

As long as the compound being steam distilled is thermally stable at the temperature involved, a chemical change due to possible reaction with water is not likely because of the very short time that the hot vapor is in contact with the steam. For example, 1-naphth-onitrile can be steam distilled at 300°C without appreciable hy-drolysis.

The steam distillate is then worked up by extraction and the product **I** *purified by vacuum distillation, crystallization, or both.*

II. Synthesis of 1-Naphthonitrile

The objective of this experiment is to convert 1-chloronaphthalene to 1-naphthonitrile. The technique involved is superheated steam distillation.

The replacement of aryl halides by the cyano group is a useful reaction that can be performed under widely different conditions [6]. Dimethylformamide [6a] and *N*-methylpyrrolidone [6b] have been found advantageous as solvents. Chlorides, bromides, and iodides have all been used as the halide.

$$ArX + CuCN \xrightarrow{\Delta} ArCN + CuX$$

After the reaction has been completed, the product is usually isolated by extraction with ether or ether–benzene. These extractions are often time consuming and difficult to effect because the reaction mixtures are quite dark, and it is difficult to see the layers. Frequently, insoluble copper complexes separate and make the separation into two layers difficult. Several methods which help in the solubilization of the copper complexes are described [6a]. The advantage of removing the aryl cyanide by superheated steam distillation is that the cyanide is completely separated from nonvolatile copper com-plexes in one simple operation.

For the preparation of 1-naphthonitrile, the apparatus shown in Figure 8-2 is suggested. About 60 g (0.7 mole) of cuprous cyanide (technical grade as supplied by the J. T. Baker Co. is satisfactory) is stirred into 150 ml of freshly distilled *N*-methylpyrrolidone in a 500-ml round-bottomed flask A fitted with a two-way adapter B which contains the stirrer C and the Hershberg distilling-reflux condenser D (compare Figure 1-5, page 20). To this mixture is added 81.3 g (0.5 mole) of 1-chloronaphthalene.

It is advisable to check the purity of the halide used before proceeding with the reaction. 1-Bromonaphthalene may also be used.

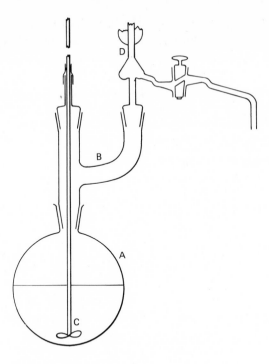

Figure 8-2. Flask with two-way adapter.

Hold at reflux for 7 hr. During the last two hours allow about 125 ml of N-methylpyrrolidone to distil through a small fractionating column. After this the reaction mixture, which darkens considerably during the heating period, is ready for processing.

The contents of flask A are submitted to superheated steam distillation at 270–300°C in the apparatus shown in Figure 8-1 as described before (page 158).

The advantage of the adapter B is that when the reaction is ready for working up flask A of Figure 8-2 can be detached and used directly as flask A of Figure 8-1 for the superheated steam distillation.

The rate at which steam is admitted at the start should be low so that the reaction mixture is not splashed into the adapter B. As soon as the remaining solvent has been steamed off, the danger of splashing is no longer a threat. When the contents of flask A appear to be entirely solid (and gray-green in color), the distillation is terminated. The time involved for a 0.5-mole run is 30–60 min.

The 1-naphthonitrile is now isolated by extraction into ether–benzene and is worked up in the usual way. Pure 1-naphthonitrile is colorless and melts at about 32°C. It should be stored in a narrow-mouth glass-stoppered bottle.

REFERENCES

[1] Zincke, T., and R. Suhl, *Ber.*, **39**, 4152 (1906).

[2] See Newman, M. S., and J. A. Eberwein, *J. Org. Chem.*, **29**, 2516 (1964) and the references therein for a review of the chemistry of such chlorinated dienones.

[3] Newman, M. S., D. Pawellek, and S. Ramachandran, *J. Amer. Chem. Soc.*, **84**, 995 (1962).

[4] Newman, M. S., and A. G. Pinkus, *J. Org. Chem.*, **19**, 978 (1954).

[5] Newman, M. S., and L. L. Wood, *J. Amer. Chem. Soc.*, **81**, 6450 (1959).

[6] See (a) Friedman, L., and H. Shechter, *J. Org. Chem.*, **26**, 2522 (1961), and (b) Newman, M. S., and H. Boden, *J. Org. Chem.*, **26**, 2525 (1961) for details and many other references.

Nine

Photolysis of 4,4-Diphenyl-2-cyclohexenone

The photolysis of 4,4-diphenyl-2-cyclohexenone to produce a mixture of *cis*- and *trans*-5,6-diphenylbicyclo[3.1.0]hexan-2-one and

their separation by chromatography are described. Before describing the specific conditions for this experiment, a few statements regarding preparative organic photochemistry are in order.

Preparative Organic Photochemistry

1. Introduction

Extensive investigations in organic photochemistry in the period 1960–1970 have led to the discovery of many new and interesting reactions [1]. Photochemistry has opened new horizons for organic synthesis, as one-step routes are often available to compounds which can be prepared only with laborious efforts via alternate procedures. The purpose here is to discuss some of the considerations which must be weighed when utlizing photochemical reactions for preparative processes.

Direct irradiation. There are two general types of synthetically useful photochemical reactions. In order to understand these two methods of producing excited molecules, a review of some elementary aspects of excited states is useful.

Most organic molecules exist in the ground state with all their electrons paired. Direct absorption of a photon by a molecule (direct irradiation) leads first to an excited singlet state. The singlet state formed has available several alternatives for decay: return to the ground state without reaction; reaction to yield a product; or intersystem crossing to the excited triplet state. Likewise the triplet state, populated by intersystem crossing, may react to give products or may decay to the ground state. The products obtained from direct excitation of a molecule may derive from either the excited singlet or triplet state, but the mechanistic aspects of photochemical transformations will not be discussed here [2].

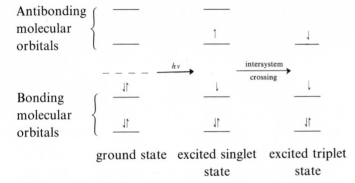

Antibonding molecular orbitals

Bonding molecular orbitals

hv

intersystem crossing

ground state   excited singlet state   excited triplet state

Sensitized irradiation. Synthetically useful photochemical reactions of organic molecules often derive from the excited triplet state. However, many molecules do not undergo efficient intersystem crossing (for example, olefinic systems) on direct irradiation. Upon direct excitation other molecules yield several products, which may be derived from the excited singlet or triplet state. In order to surmount these complications, an alternate method is often used. This method employs a sensitizer (photochemical catalyst) to selectively populate the triplet state of a second molecule (the substrate). The steps involved in the sensitization are: excitation of the sensitizer to its excited singlet state (equation 9.1); intersystem crossing of the sensitizer singlet to the triplet state (equation 9.2); and triplet energy transfer from the sensitizer to the substrate to yield the excited triplet state of the substrate (equation 9.3).

$$\text{Sen} \xrightarrow{\;hv\;} \text{Sen}^{*1} \qquad\qquad\qquad\qquad \textbf{9.1}$$

$$\text{Sen}^{*1} \xrightarrow[\text{crossing}]{\text{intersystem}} \text{Sen}^{*3} \qquad\qquad\qquad \textbf{9.2}$$

$$\text{Sen}^{*3} + \text{substrate} \longrightarrow \text{substrate}^{*3} + \text{Sen.} \qquad \textbf{9.3}$$

2. Selection of a Sensitizer

Experimental factors. To utilize triplet sensitization techniques, several fundamental principles should be understood. In a sensitization experiment, the incident irradiation should be captured almost entirely (95–99%) by the sensitizer. The ultraviolet spectrum of both the sensitizer and the substrate (the molecule to be sensitized) must therefore be known. The conditions for 95–99% absorption of light by a sensitizer can be guaranteed by adjusting the concentration of sensitizer and the wavelength of the exciting light. A useful guideline for establishing when the sensitizer is absorbing nearly all of the incident irradiation is to calculate the concentration of sensitizer necessary to absorb 95 % of the light at the wavelength where the $^\varepsilon$substrate/$^\varepsilon$sensitizer is maximum. The percent light capture is conveniently calculated by means of the following equation, where $^\varepsilon\lambda$ is the extinction coefficient at the wavelength λ and c is the concentration.

$$\text{Percent light capture}_{\text{Sen }\lambda} = \frac{^\varepsilon\lambda_{\text{Sen}}c_{\text{Sen}}}{^\varepsilon\lambda_{\text{Sen}}c_{\text{Sen}} + {}^\varepsilon\lambda_{\text{sub}}c_{\text{sub}}} \times 100$$

An ideal triplet sensitizer should have the following properties: (a) strong ultraviolet absorption where the substrate absorption is weak; (b) a very short-lived singlet state so singlet energy transfer (singlet sensitization) does not occur; (c) a high efficiency of intersystem crossing; (d) sufficient triplet energy to populate the triplet state of the substrate; and (e) low photochemical reactivity relative to energy transfer. A complete discussion of these points is outside the scope of this article [3]; however, (a) has already been briefly considered (see above). The aromatic ketone sensitizers listed in Table 9-1 admirably fulfill requirements (b) and (c).

Table 9–1.   Triplet Energies of Selected Sensitizers

SENSITIZER	E_T (kcal/mole)
Acetone	>75
Acetophenone	74
Benzophenone	69
4,4'-Bis(dimethylamino)benzophenone	61
2-Acetonaphthone	59

One of the most important points in the selection of a sensitizer is to ensure that triplet energy is transferred to the substrate molecule. The efficiency of energy transfer is expressed as follows:

(1) $\text{Sen} \xrightarrow{hv} \text{Sen}^{*1}$

(2) $\text{Sen}^{*1} \longrightarrow \text{Sen}^{*3}$

(3) $\text{Sen}^{*3} \xrightarrow{k_d} \text{Sen}$

(4) $\text{Sen}^{*3} + \text{sub} \xrightarrow{k_t} \text{Sen} + \text{sub}^{*3}$

where k_d = rate constant for decay of excited sensitizer to its ground state; and k_t = rate constant for energy transfer.

$$\% \text{ Efficiency of energy transfer} = \frac{k_t[\text{substrate}] \times 100}{k_t[\text{substrate}] + k_d}$$

Thus, a knowledge of k_t and k_d allows one to adjust the substrate concentration so that triplet energy transfer would be highly efficient. In practice a compromise must be made; the substrate is used in sufficient concentration to insure reasonably efficient energy transfer, but not in so high a concentration as to absorb directly the incident irradiation.

For sensitization work, then, a knowledge of the values for k_t and k_d is informative. A number of studies on the dependence of k_t on the exothermicity of the energy transfer reaction have led to the data presented in Table 9-2 [4]. The useful generalization emerging is that, when the triplet energy of the sensitizer exceeds that of the substrate by greater than 3 kcal/mole, the rate of energy transfer approximates the rate of diffusion. Typically the rate of diffusion in common organic solvents is 10^9–10^{10} liter/mole sec.

Table 9–2. Rate of Triplet Energy Transfer as a Function of Exothermicity

ΔE	energy difference between sensitizer and substrate level	k_t (liter/mole sec)
	3–22 kcal/mole	10^9–10^{10}
	1–3 kcal/mole	10^6–10^8
	Endothermic	10^3–10^4

Unfortunately there is no extensive information on the rates of decay of carbonyl triplets at room temperature. The decay rates for benzophenone and acetophenone in benzene at room temperature are about 10^5 sec^{-1} [5]. Use of this value, $k_t = 10^9$ liter/mole sec, and a substrate concentration of 10^{-2} M, allows the calculation of a triplet energy transfer efficiency of about 99%.

$\%$ Effectiveness of energy transfer

$$= \frac{[10^9 \text{ liter/mole sec}][10^{-2} \text{ mole/liter}] \times 100}{[10^9 \text{ liter/mole sec } 10^{-2} \text{ mole/liter}] + [10^5 \text{ sec}^{-1}]} = 99$$

A final consideration is the photostability of the sensitizer itself. Although the photosensitizer should be photostable, no compound ideally fits this requirement. Of the sensitizers listed in Table 9-1 the first three undergo photoreduction in the excited triplet state. Fortunately, the bimolecular rate constant for photoreduction is 10^3–10^4 lower than that for efficient energy transfer. Thus, photoreduction is minimized if the concentration of substrate is high.

Note that this factor of 10^3–10^4 is dampened considerably if the solvent is the hydrogen donor.

Also, solvents which are poor hydrogen donors (benzene, for example) are preferable when benzophenone and acetophenone are used as sensitizers. The photoreduction problem is completely absent in the case of the lower energy sensitizers 4,4'-bis(dimethylamino)benzophenone and 2-acetonaphthone. However, although these compounds are less reactive and more strongly absorbing in the near ultraviolet region, they suffer from having much lower triplet energies. This makes them ideal sensitizers for substrates having low triplet energies but almost useless for compounds having triplet energies greater than 59 kcal/mole. In summary, a sensitizer should be selected which best fits the criteria discussed above. Planning a Sensitized Photochemical Reaction, a later section, amplifies the discussion presented here.

3. Choice of Solvent

Although in principle almost any solvent can be, and has been, used for photochemical reactions, a desirable solvent should be easily purified, transparent in the irradiation region, and unreactive towards photochemical intermediates formed in the reaction (unless, of course, solvent participation leads to the desired product). Another desirable property is that the solvent should dissolve not only the starting material and product but also any minor amounts of polymer which might be formed in the reaction. Thus, polymeric material is prevented from coating the walls of the reaction vessel and scattering useful light, which would lengthen the time needed for irradiation.

Some photochemical reactions are markedly influenced by solvents. The best solvent for a particular reaction sometimes must be found by trial and error. However, two potential problems must be mentioned. First, solvents which are good hydrogen donors (for example, isopropyl alcohol, diethyl ether) can be especially troublesome in cases where the excited state is capable of a competing photoreduction reaction (see above). This problem can be acute in the photochemical reactions of carbonyl compounds. Second, solvents which are reasonably nucleophilic (for example, ethyl and methyl alcohol) also may partially divert the normal course of rearrangement by effecting undesired addition reactions which consume starting material and complicate separation of the desired product.

Two useful solvents are benzene and t-butyl alcohol. Both of these solvents are poor hydrogen atom donors to radicallike, electronically excited species and serve to minimize photoreduction processes which involve solvent participation. Benzene is especially useful in reactions sensitized by benzophenone or acetophenone since these molecules readily undergo photoreduction. One disadvantage of benzene is that its short ultraviolet cutoff (280 nm) prevents it from being used in the shorter wavelength region. On the other hand, t-butyl alcohol has a good transmittance range in the ultraviolet and serves as a moderately polar, poorly nucleophilic medium for photochemical reactions. However, its melting point (25°C) limits its usefulness at low temperatures.

4. Concentration Factors

The most effective concentration of solute to be photolyzed in the chosen solvent should be determined according to knowledge of the molecularity of the desired reaction. If the reaction is bimolecular, the concentration of reactants should be high enough to allow collision of the molecules during the lifetime of the excited state. Typical concentrations used in the literature vary from 0.1–1.0 M. In some cases, too high a concentration is disadvantageous because an excited molecule may be quenched by a ground state molecule. When the desired reaction is unimolecular, the reaction can be run at any concentration, provided bimolecular processes do not compete. Typically these reactions are run at concentrations from 10^{-3}–10^{-1} M.

5. Photochemical Light Sources

Proper selection of a light source and proper filtration of the irradiation emitted often determines whether or not a reaction is synthetically useful [6]. Although it is desirable to know the exact wavelength-intensity distribution of light sources, this information is seldom available since aging in any lamp often changes both the overall output and its wavelength distribution. Although the published wavelength-intensity distribution curves are not quantitative, they aid in selecting a suitable light source for reactions.

Two methods are commonly used to obtain light of useful wavelength distribution in preparative organic photochemistry. The first involves use of a medium- or high-pressure mercury source [6] and removal of the undesirable wavelengths by glass or solution filters. These sources have the advantage of high intensity and a near continuum output of irradiation throughout the ultraviolet and visible regions of the spectrum. Probably the most convenient method for filtration is to surround the light source with a glass filter (see Figure 9-8). The typical transmittance curves [7] shown in Figure 9-1 illustrate that these filters suffice as ultraviolet cutoffs for the short wavelength irradiation but do not cut off at the long wavelength edge. Thus, such filters function well, provided the

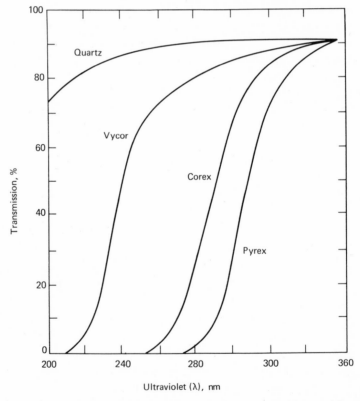

Figure 9-1. Typical curves for quartz, vycor, corex, and pyrex. (*Courtesy New England Ultraviolet Company, Middletown, Conn.*)

An Advanced Organic Laboratory Course

longer wavelength light does not photolyze the photochemical product(s).

A second general type of system employs sources which emit only in a given region of the ultraviolet spectrum. These lamps provide more flexibility in adapting the light source to the photochemical system. The spectral output from a low-pressure mercury lamp (mainly 2537 Å) is shown in Figure 9-2, that from a "sunlight phosphor" in Figure 9-3, and that from a "blacklight phosphor" in Figure 9-4. The examples which follow illustrate how the photochemical system dictates the choice of light source.

6. Maintenance of an Inert Atmosphere

One important consideration in conducting a photolysis is to maintain an inert atmosphere during the course of the reaction. This is commonly done in two ways: degassing the sample *via* freeze-pump-thaw cycles; or bubbling a gentle stream of inert gas through the stirred reaction mixture. Although the latter method is much

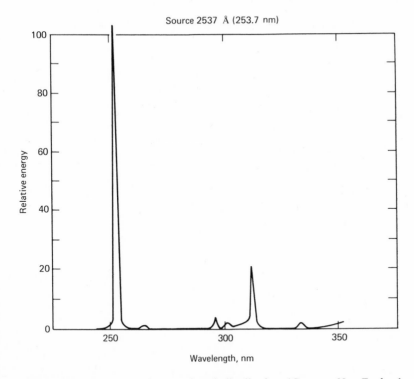

Figure 9-2. Representative wavelength distribution. (*Courtesy New England Ultraviolet Company, Middletown, Conn.*)

Photolysis of 4,4-Diphenyl-2-cyclohexenone　　　　**171**

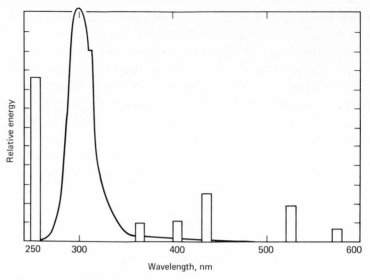

Figure 9-3. Representative wavelength distribution of "sunlight phosphor." (*Courtesy New England Ultraviolet Company, Middletown, Conn.*)

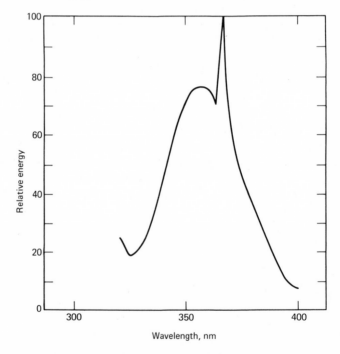

Figure 9-4. Representative wavelength distribution of "blacklight phosphor." (*Courtesy New England Ultraviolet Company, Middletown, Conn.*)

less efficient in removing oxygen, it is very convenient and suitable for all but the most oxygen-sensitive systems. The common methods for maintaining an inert atmosphere in an immersion apparatus involve bubbling the inert gas through a polyethylene tube run into the reaction mixture or passing nitrogen gently through a glass frit sealed in the bottom of the photolysis vessel (see Figure 9-8).

7. Temperature Control

Temperature, usually a critical factor in common organic reactions, has been subject to little systematic study in preparative organic photochemistry. Perhaps 90% of the photolyses carried out in organic chemistry are run at temperatures between 10° and 45°C. Thus, most preparative photochemical reactors make little provision for variable temperature control. If the reaction is to be refluxed, an ordinary heating mantle or oil bath can be used around the reaction vessel with a condenser attached at the top. For cooling, the lower part of the photochemical reactor may be immersed in a controlled low-temperature bath. Photolysis at low temperature is especially important if the starting material or photoproduct is likely to be thermally unstable. When water is circulating through the lamp it is critical to adjust the water flow so as to prevent freezing of the water and ensuing damage to the lamp and reaction vessel.

8. Stirring

The last point to be noted involves effective stirring which may be a critical factor in some reactions. Ordinarily, magnetic stirring is sufficient except when a large volume (more than 1 liter) of reaction mixture is involved. In this case an oversized stirring bar should be used to ensure effective mixing of the reactor contents.

Stirring by means of a fairly rapid stream of inert gas is often effective, provided the solvent is not too volatile at the temperature involved.

Monitoring of Reaction Progress

Once the reaction is in progress the remaining consideration is to monitor the course of the photolysis by some analytical method. Monitoring is necessary even when following a literature preparation, since the lamp output may vary depending on the line voltage and lamp age. The analytical technique to be employed is dependent on the nature of the starting material and products. However, thin layer chromatography, vapor phase chromatography, and ultraviolet methods are especially useful. The first time a reaction is run, the change of ultraviolet spectrum of the photolysis mixture should be followed. This is important even though another method is chosen for monitoring the reaction in later runs. Ultraviolet monitoring is important because some photochemical reactions develop minor amounts of intensely absorbing impurities as the reaction proceeds. If the impurity captures nearly all the incident irradiation, the impression may be gained that the starting material is exceptionally unreactive. By closely studying the ultraviolet spectrum, the development of a light-capturing impurity becomes discernible. In some instances, changing a reaction condition (for example, solvent) may eliminate or reduce the problem. At worst, it becomes clear that the sluggish photochemistry observed is not the inherent photolability of the compound but rather an experimental difficulty.

A case in point is the slow rearrangement of 4,4-diphenyl-2-5-cyclohexadienone in benzene versus its rapid photolysis in dioxane-water. Monitoring the ultraviolet spectrum of the reaction in benzene indicated the development of an intense absorption in the near ultraviolet, whereas the run in dioxane-water showed the expected ultraviolet absorption. It was later discovered that a ketene was produced in minor amounts during the photolysis. In dioxane-water, the ketene was trapped as the acid and caused no further trouble. However, in benzene, the ketene underwent further photolysis to produce strongly absorbing material which reduced the light absorbed by the starting material.

Planning a Sensitized Photochemical Reaction

The photosensitized cycloaddition of two olefinic units, with resultant production of a four-membered ring, is often a synthetically useful photochemical reaction. Here some of the principles in planning or scaling up a sensitized photolysis can be illustrated by considering the hypothetical photoaddition of indene triplet to a simple olefin. In this case, a sensitizer must be chosen for populating the indene triplet excited state (the triplet energy of the simple olefin being much higher than that of indene). The first step involves consideration of all sensitizers which, from energy considerations, would efficiently populate the indene triplet. The triplet energy of indene is reported as 59 kcal/mole [8]. If this value were not available in the literature, an analogous chromophore could be selected as a model (in this case β-methylstyrene, $E_T = 61.8$ kcal/mole) [9]. Taking the triplet energy as 59 kcal/mole and noting that diffusion-controlled energy transfer would occur from sensitizers having greater than 62 kcal/mole, it is apparent that acetone, acetophenone, or benzophenone fulfill the energy requirement (Table 9-1). Figure 9-5 shows the ultraviolet spectra for acetone, acetophenone, benzophenone, and indene. Since indene shows only weak absorption below 300 nm, any of the sensitizers could be employed, although acetone would have to be used in high concentration (that is, as solvent) because of its low extinction coefficient. The choice of sensitizer at this point depends largely upon the ease of separation of the reaction products from the sensitizer. Workers in the literature have employed acetophone, benzophenone, and acetone as sensitizers and acetone, 95% ethanol, and benzene as solvents [10].

Photolysis of 4,4-Diphenyl-2-cyclohexenone

Synthetically useful direct photolyses generally meet one or both of the following conditions: (a) the photoproduct of interest has an ultraviolet absorption spectrum sufficiently different from that of the starting material so that very little incident irradiation is absorbed during the course of the photolysis; and (b) the photoproduct, although absorbing light, is photochemically stable under the reaction conditions. Hence, one method of optimizing the yield of a photochemical product is to select the wavelength of irradiation where the starting material has strong absorption as compared to weak or no absorption by the product. Unfortunately, it is difficult to obtain high-intensity sources of monochromatic light; therefore, this condition is only partially satisfied unless a sophisticated light-filtering system is available.

Although optimum conditions for a photochemical reaction are dictated by the particular substrate being irradiated, some of the general principles involved in planning a photochemical reaction can be illustrated in the photolysis of 4,4-diphenyl-2-cyclohexenone.

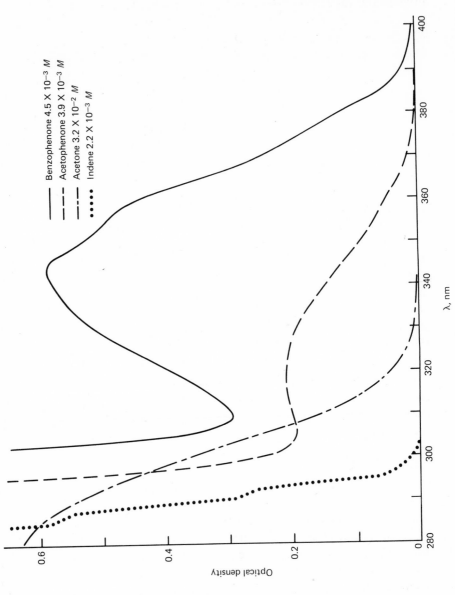

Figure 9-5. Ultraviolet spectra of indene and sensitizers in benzene.

Benzophenone 4.5 × 10⁻³ M
Acetophenone 3.9 × 10⁻³ M
Acetone 3.2 × 10⁻² M
Indene 2.2 × 10⁻³ M

The photolysis of **I** yields the cyclopropyl ketones **II** and **III** [11].

The ratio of the ketones produced is dependent upon the length of irradiation and the excitation wavelength, since the major kinetic product **II** is photoisomerized to **III**.

$$\quad\text{I}\qquad\qquad\qquad\text{II}\qquad\qquad\qquad\text{III}$$

The first step in any photochemical experiment is the measurement of the ultraviolet absorption of the material to be photolyzed. It is also extremely informative to have the ultraviolet absorption data of the photoproducts. Often a sample of the product is not available; in this case model chromophores are valuable in estimating its ultraviolet absorption. Figure 9-6 shows the ultraviolet absorption spectra of **I**, **II**, and **III** in benzene solution. Ideally one should irradiate **I** with light of wavelength greater than 320 nm, as this would be readily absorbed by **I** and largely transmitted by **II** and **III**. An ideal light source would be the "blacklight" phosphor (see Figure 9-4) because it shows strong emission from 330–400 nm. However, since the photoproducts themselves are relatively photostable (except for cis-trans isomerization), Pyrex-filtered light (ultraviolet cutoff 290 nm) from a conventional medium- or high-pressure mercury source could also be employed.

Having chosen a suitable light source, there remains selection of the solvent and execution of the reaction. In order to minimize photoreduction and nucleophilic addition reactions of excited **I**, benzene is a logical choice. Furthermore, it is always useful to follow the course of the photochemical reaction by some analytical technique, as the time required for complete consumption of starting material will vary with the nature of the light source. For this particular reaction, two methods are especially useful: vapor phase chromatography and thin layer chromatography (neutral alumina 40% adsorbent, ether-hexane as eluent). Figure 9-7 shows the progress of the photolysis when followed by flame ionization gas

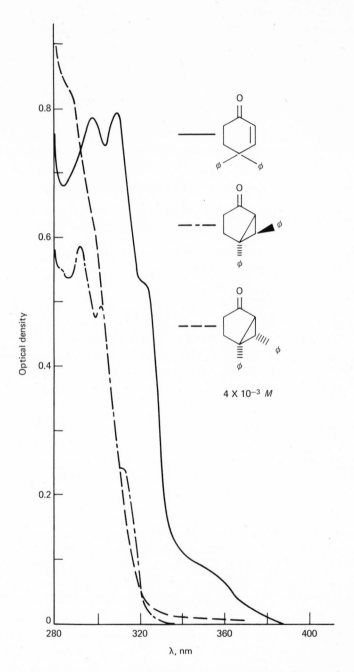

4×10^{-3} M

Figure 9-6. Ultraviolet spectra of starting material and photoproducts in benzene.

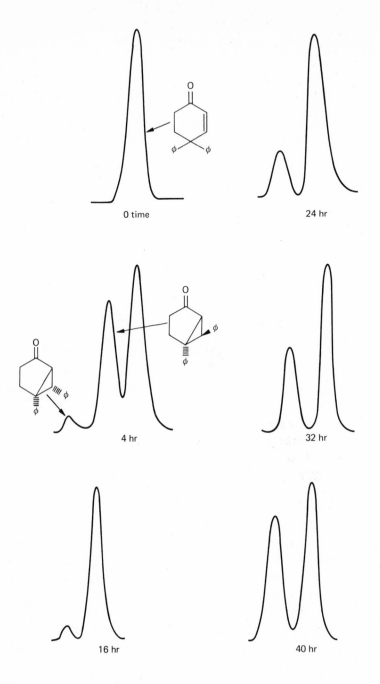

Figure 9-7. Progress of photolysis of 4,4-diphenylcyclohex-2-en-1-one (12 g in 1 liter of benzene), followed by vapor phase chromatography.

chromatography on a 5-ft by 1/8-in. column containing 5% SE-30 (a silicon) on 80/120 Mesh Varaport 30 at 150°C.

A satisfactory prepacked column is obtainable from The Varian Aerograph Co.

The separation of the two photoproducts is followed by conventional Silica Gel chromatography.

The silica gel, 80–200 mesh, was obtained from The Davidson Chemical Co.

The experimental description of the reaction which follows is meant only to be illustrative of the type of results obtained.

Experimental Technique

The length of this experiment can be adjusted to the time available and the needs of the student.

4,4-Diphenyl-2-cyclohexenone may be purchased from Arapahoe Chemical Co., Boulder, Colorado, or synthesized from diphenyl-acetaldehyde (Chemical Samples Co., Columbus, Ohio) and methyl vinyl ketone in a one-step condensation reaction [12]. If it is desirable to introduce a synthetic sequence into the experiment, the starting enone can be synthesized in three steps from benzil. The experiment which follows describes: the general photolysis procedure; the synthesis of 4,4-diphenyl-2-cyclohexenone from benzil; its photolysis; and the chromatographic separation of the two photoketones. Although the first two synthetic steps are described for a large-scale preparation, reducing the quantities involved by a factor of ten has little influence on yield.

Hydrobenzoin. To a solution of 300 g (1.40 mole) of benzil in 1.5 ml of 95% ethanol brought to 15°C is added 37.8 g (1.0 mole) of sodium borohydride portionwise over a period of 1 hr, keeping the temperature below 24°C. After stirring the reaction mixture for 2 hr at 25°C, 1 liter of water is added and the mixture is heated at reflux for 1 hr. Cooling and addition of water just prior to incipient cloudiness yields white plates which are filtered and dried. After final drying in a vacuum oven at 60°C, 233 g (76%) of white plates of hydrobenzoin, mp 137–139.5°C, is obtained. Concentration of the mother liquors yields an additional 25 g of slightly less pure product.

Diphenylacetaldehyde. A solution of 233 g (1.1 mole) of hydro-benzoin and 23 g of *p*-toluenesulfonic acid in 3 l of dry benzene is stirred and refluxed under nitrogen for 48 hr. The resulting water is collected in a Dean–Stark trap (see page 10). Filter the reaction mixture and follow by washing with 5 % sodium bicarbonate, water, and saturated sodium chloride solution. Dry over sodium sulfate, and remove the solvent *in vacuo*. The yield is 185 g of yellow oil. Add 0.1 g of hydroquinone and fractionate through a short column to obtain 120 g (55 %) of diphenylacetaldehyde, bp 148–153°C (0.4 mm). A dark yellow viscous oil remains in the pot after distillation.

4,4-Diphenyl-2-cyclohexenone. A mixture of 3.6 g (0.05 mole) of freshly distilled methyl vinyl ketone and 10.0 g (0.05 mole) of diphenylacetaldehyde in 70 ml of ether is cooled to 5°C in an ice bath. To this cooled, stirred solution is added alcoholic potassium hydroxide dropwise [0.88 g (0.016 mole) of potassium hydroxide (85 %) in 5.6 ml of ethanol] over a period of 0.5 hr at such a rate as to maintain the temperature below 10°C. The ice bath is then removed and the light yellow reaction mixture stirred for 1 hr while warming to room temperature (a solid may precipitate at this point). After addition of 50 ml of benzene to dissolve the solid, the mixture is neutralized to litmus paper with 3 *N* hydrochloric acid. The benzene layer is separated and the aqueous layer extracted twice with 50 ml portions of ether. The combined extracts are washed with 50 ml of saturated salt solution, dried over calcium sulfate, and con-centrated *in vacuo*. The crude product is a gummy oil which is re-crystallized from 95 % ethanol to yield 9.1 g (72 %) of light yellow crystals of 4,4-diphenyl-2-cyclohexenone, mp 92–93°C, in two crops. Yields generally run 65–83 %.

Irradiation procedure. The essential elements of a photochemical immersion apparatus are shown in Figure 9-8. For photolysis, the material is dissolved in a minimum volume of solvent and trans-ferred to the photolysis cell A which contains a magnetic stirrer B. The cell A is then fitted with the immersion well C which contains inlet D and outlet E for water circulation and is secured firmly by clamp F.

Immersion wells made from quartz are quite expensive (about $250). However, if Pyrex-filtered light is to be used for photolysis, Pyrex

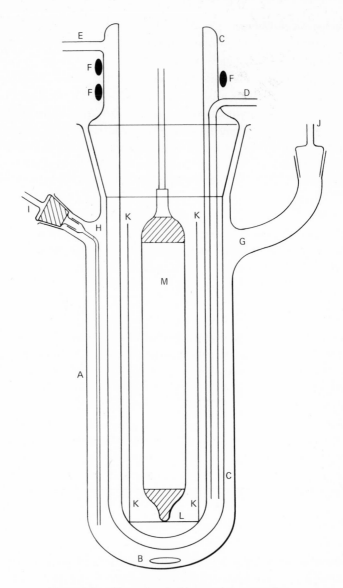

Figure 9-8. Photochemical immersion apparatus.

immersion wells are satisfactory. Commercial units are commonly available.

Additional solvent can now be added to the irradiation flask through the side arm G (a liquid level up to G is convenient). The stirring is started and purified nitrogen is gently bubbled into the stirred solution through a flexible polyethylene tube H attached to the glass insert I as shown. A diffusion tube J serves as exit for the gas.

A diffusion tube is prepared by coiling a 9–12 in. length of 1–2 mm capillary tubing.

Generally, the nitrogen flow is commenced 1/2 to 3/4 hr prior to irradiation and continued during the length of the photolysis. Finally, the desired filter sleeve K is inserted to rest on asbestos ring L in the well followed by the lamp M.

An asbestos ring cut from an ordinary asbestos pad is placed at the bottom of the immersion well to minimize the chance of breakage during insertion and removal of the sleeve. The lamp should always be handled by the ends because fingerprints on the quartz surface burn in during use and result in etching of the lamp.

If the apparatus is to be used in a hood or open area, it should be covered with aluminum foil to prevent transmitted light from damaging the eyes of other people in the room. Once the system is degassed, the water is turned on so that a gentle stream exits from the outlet E, and the lamp is started.

Since a combination of water and electricity is potentially dangerous, hoses should be securely fastened. Furthermore, unless provision is made for automatically shutting off the lamp in case of water stoppage, the apparatus should not be left unattended for long periods (see page 221).

Photolysis of 4,4-Diphenyl-2-cyclohexenone. A solution of 3.0 g (12 mM) of ketone in 300 ml of benzene is irradiated under a nitrogen atmosphere with Pyrex-filtered light from a Hanovia 450-watt medium-pressure source for 20 hr. The progress of the reaction is followed by vapor pressure chromatography and thin layer chromatography. After 20 hr of irradiation, the starting material disappears. Removal of the benzene on the rotary evaporator yields a light-yellow viscous oil which may be chromatographed on a 2.5 × 60 cm column of Silica Gel (Davidson Grade 950, 69–200 mesh) slurry packed (see page 50) in 5% ether-hexane. The column is eluted in 250 ml fractions and yields the following results: fractions 1–2, 5% ether-hexane, nil; 3–6, 7% ether-hexane, nil; 6–13, 10% ether-hexane, 1.85 g of the *trans*-5,6-diphenylbicyclo[3.1.0]hexan-2-one; 13–15, 10% ether-hexane, nil; 16–22, 10% ether-hexane, 0.39 g of *cis*-5,6-diphenylbicyclo[3.1.0]hexan-2-one. Throughout the chromatography, the fractions are checked for homogeneity by thin layer chromatography. Recrystallization of the *trans*-5,6-diphenylbicyclo[3.1.0]hexan-2-one from 95% ethanol yields 1.60 g (53%) of white crystalline material, mp 74–76°C. Recrystallization of *cis*-5,6-diphenylbicyclo[3.1.0]hexan-2-one from ethanol yields 0.21 g (7%) of white crystals, mp 113–115°C.

Instead of purification by column chromatography, the desired cis- and trans compounds may be isolated (on a smaller scale) by means of preparative thin layer chromatography (see page 70).

REFERENCES

[1] For elementary reviews of basic transformations of olefins and ketones, see Swenton, J. S., *J. Chem. Educ.*, **46**, 7, 217 (1969).

[2] For an excellent discussion, see Calvert, J. G., and J. N. Pitts, *Photochemistry*, John Wiley and Sons, Inc., New York, 1966, chap. 6.

[3] For an excellent discussion of complications in sensitizations see Engel, P. S., and B. M. Monroe in W. A. Noyes, G. S. Hammond, and J. N. Pitts (eds.), *Advances in Photochemistry*, vol. 8, Interscience Publishers, New York, in press.

[4] Wilkinson, F., in W. A. Noyes, G. S. Hammond, and J. N. Pitts (eds.), *Advances in Photochemistry*, vol. 3, Interscience Publishers, New York, 1964, pp. 241–268.

[5] Clark, W. D. K., A. D. Litt, and C. Steel, *J. Amer. Chem. Soc.*, **91**, 5413 (1969).

[6] For an extensive discussion of experimental techniques in photochemistry, see ref. 2, pp. 686–809.

[7] These curves are supplied through the courtesy of the New England Ultraviolet Company, Middletown, Conn.

[8] Heckman, R. C., *J. Mol. Spectrosc.*, **2**, 27 (1958).

[9] Evans, D. F., *J. Chem. Soc.*, 1351 (1957); Lamola, A. A., and G. S. Hammond, *J. Chem. Phys.*, **43**, 2129 (1965).

[10] Anastassiou, A. G., F. L. Setliff, and G. W. Griffin, *J. Org. Chem.*, **31**, 2705 (1966); Metzner, W., and W. Hartman, *Chem. Ber.*, **101**, 4099 (1968); McCullough, J. J., and C. W. Huang, *Can. J. Chem.*, **47**, 757 (1969); Bowman, R. M., J. J. McCullough, and J. S. Swenton, *Can. J. Chem.*, **47**, 4503 (1969).

[11] Zimmerman, H. E., and J. W. Wilson, *J. Amer. Chem. Soc.*, **86**, 4036 (1964); Zimmerman, H. E., and K. G. Hancock, *J. Amer. Chem. Soc.*, **90**, 3749 (1968).

[12] Zimmerman, H. E., R. Keese, J. Nasielski, and J. S. Swenton, *J. Amer. Chem. Soc.*, **88**, 4895 (1966).

Ten

Ozonization of (−)-β-Pinene to (+)-Nopinone

In this experiment the preparation of an optically active ketone by ozonation of an optically active olefin is illustrated [1]. Before starting this experiment the excellent review article [1] on ozonization should be consulted.

β-pinene $\xrightarrow[CH_3OH]{O_3}$ ozonide $\xrightarrow[NaI]{CH_3COOH}$ nopinone

When ozone comes into contact with an olefin an initial ozonide **I** is formed in which a bond remains between the two carbons originally linked by the double bond. This initial ozonide undergoes cleavage to form a dipolar ion, **II**, and a carbonyl compound, **III**. The fragments **II** and **III** then combine to form the ozonide, **IV**. It is also possible for two dipolar ions, **II**, to combine to form either a cyclic peroxide, **V**, or a polymeric peroxide, **VI**. If the original olefin is unsymmetrical, a variety of different oxonides and peroxides is possible [2].

Ozonization is often narrowly regarded only as a means of proving structure of unsaturated compounds. However, many valuable compounds may be obtained by ozonization of appropriate precursors. The present experiment illustrates the use of ozonation in the preparation of (+)-nopinone [3].

The material to be ozonized, (−)-β-pinene, is readily available. The choice of a solvent for ozonization is important. If the ozonization is to be carried out at low temperatures (about −70°C), the solvent should be able to dissolve not only the starting material but also the ozonide or any peroxide substances that may be formed during the ozonization at that temperature [1]. Methanol is an excellent solvent for the ozonization of pinene [2].

The formation of an insoluble substance on the walls of the reaction vessel during ozonization is a sign that great care should be exercised in the workup. Such solids are often peroxides and may be explosive.

A solution of (−)-β-pinene (15–20 g) in methanol (120–150 ml) is ozonized at −70°C (cooling by dry ice–acetone). The time required is dictated by the rate of production of ozone, as the ozone is quantitatively absorbed (except at the very end). In this ozonization careful control of the amount of ozone used is not important because excess ozone does not react with the ozonide formed. Oxygen streams containing 2–4% of ozone are convenient to use.

The methods of determining the ozone content of a stream of oxygen are described [1]. A description of apparatus and the variation of ozone concentration as a function of rate of oxygen flow, secondary voltage on the transformer used, and other variables is available [4]. Ozonizers of the Henne-Perilstein type [3] and an ozonizer obtained from the Welsbach Company, Philadelphia, Pa., have been found satisfactory at Ohio State.

The methanolic solution resulting from the ozonization is treated with a solution containing a small excess of sodium iodide and acetic acid in methanol. The iodide liberated by the reductive cleavage of all peroxidic linkages present [1], is destroyed by the addition of sufficient sodium bisulfite. After making basic with sodium carbonate, the product is extracted with ether-benzene as described (see page 14). When the solvent is distilled off, (+)-nopinone is obtained as a colorless liquid with a boiling point in the 80–85°C region at 11–12 mm, in 70–78 % yield.

The yield and the rotation depend upon the source of β-(−)-pinene. (+)-Nopinone, $[\alpha]_D^{25} + 18.4°$, has been reported [2].

For a variety of reductive and oxidative procedures for workup of solutions resulting from ozonolysis, consult the review article by Bailey [1]. A recent excellent method of decomposition of ozonides to yield aldehydes which employs dimethyl sulfide has been described [5].

An alternate ozonization that may be carried out involves the conversion of pyrene to 5-formyl-4-phenanthroic acid, which exists mainly in the hydroxylactone form shown [6].

REFERENCES

[1] Bailey, P. S., *Chem. Rev.*, **58**, 925 (1958).
[2] See March, J., *Advanced Organic Chemistry*, McGraw-Hill Book Co., New York, 1968, pp. 871–874, for references to recent work on the mechanism of ozonolysis.
[3] Meinwald, J., and P. G. Gassman, *J. Amer. Chem. Soc.*, **82**, 5445 (1960).
[4] Henne, A. L., and W. L. Perilstein, *J. Amer. Chem. Soc.*, **65**, 2183 (1943); *Organic Syntheses*, coll. vol. III, p. 673.
[5] Papas, J. J., W. P. Keaveney, E. Gancher, and M. Berger, *Tetrahedron Lett.*, 4273 (1966).
[6] Dessy, R. E., and M. S. Newman, *Organic Syntheses*, coll. vol. IV, p. 484.

Eleven

Preparation of Bromobenzene from *p*-Bromo- iodobenzene

The object of this experiment is selectively to reduce p-bromoiodo-benzene to bromobenzene. The technique involved is reduction by an electrochemical process as illustrated in equation (11.1) [1]. In

accomplishing this conversion a working knowledge of certain electrochemical principles will be developed.

Basic Principles of Electrochemistry

Prior to a discussion of specific details of organic electrochemistry, a few fundamental relationships merit review. The voltage imposed across a system is equal to the current (in amps) times the resistance (in ohms). This relationship is normally represented by equation (11.2).

$$\Delta E = IR \qquad\qquad 11.2$$

where ΔE is electromotive force in volts, I is the current in amps (coulombs per second) and R is the resistance in ohms. The total number of moles of electrons passed is expressed by equation (11.3).

$$\text{Moles of electrons} = \frac{\text{amps} \times \text{seconds}}{96,500 \text{ coulombs/mole}} \qquad 11.3$$

A mole of electrons is normally referred to as a Faraday.

The simplest type of electrolytic cell, drawn in Figure 11-1, consists of a direct-current power source (for example a storage battery B), an anode A, and a cathode C. The voltage is measured on the voltmeter D and the amperage on ammeter E. This functional electrolytic apparatus is sufficient for certain types of electrolytic conversions and is used in the fashion shown, with the electrodes immersed in the solution F to be electrolyzed. The solution is contained in a cell G.

If the electrolysis is carried out so that the solvent does not boil, open cells such as that shown in Figure 11-1 may be used. Cooling may be arranged by placing the cell G in a cooling bath H.

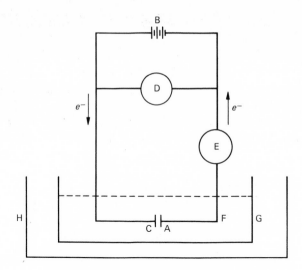

Figure 11-1. Simple electrolytic system.

Current electron flow is in the direction shown with electrons being supplied at the cathode (reduction) and electrons being removed at the anode (oxidation).

For satisfactory results many electrochemical procedures require precise control of the voltage. Such electrolyses are generally referred to as constant-potential or controlled-potential electrolyses. Controlled-potential electrolyses are required when more than one electrochemical process is possible. For instance, suppose the polarogram (current versus voltage curve) for the electrolytic reaction of a given compound is represented in Figure 11-2. Such a polarogram indicates that two distinct electron-transfer processes

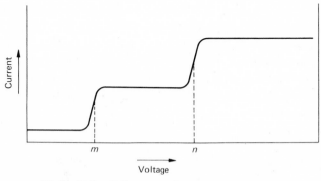

Figure 11-2. Polarogram for a two-step reaction.

are occurring, one at low voltage m and a second at higher voltage n. If the electrolysis is carried out at the higher voltage, both processes will be occurring in the electrolysis cell. If the electrolysis is performed at the lower voltage, only the low-voltage process will occur. Polarographic analysis of erythritol tetrabromide shows a curve similar to that in Figure 11-2. When the tetrabromide is electrolyzed at a voltage of n or greater, spiropentane is obtained in high yield

$$\underset{BrCH_2}{\overset{BrCH_2}{\diagdown}}C\underset{CH_2Br}{\overset{CH_2Br}{\diagup}} \xrightarrow[\text{voltage}=n\text{ or greater}]{-4e^-} \underset{CH_2}{\overset{CH_2}{|}}C\underset{CH_2}{\overset{CH_2}{|}}$$

$$+2e^- \quad \text{voltage } m \qquad\qquad \text{voltage } r \quad +2e^- \qquad \textbf{11.4}$$

$$\underset{CH_2}{\overset{CH_2}{|}}C\underset{CH_2Br}{\overset{CH_2Br}{\diagup}} \qquad \textbf{11.5}$$

(see equation 11.4). However, electrolysis at voltages less than n but greater than m produces the dibromide shown (see equation 11.5). When this dibromide is subjected to reductive electrolytic conditions where the voltage is greater than n, it is also converted to spiropentane [2]. Thus by controlling the potential at which the reaction is run, the electrochemical process which will occur can be controlled. In this way intermediates which would be difficult to prepare by other methods can often be obtained. In order to control the potential of an electrolysis, more sophisticated equipment than that described in Figure 11-1 is needed. As the difference between voltage m and n grows smaller, it becomes more difficult to separate the two electrochemical processes. Consequently, increasingly sensitive instrumentation is required. For controlled-potential electrolysis an electrolytic setup similar to that shown in Figure 11-3 is necessary. This apparatus consists of a dc power supply (for example, a storage battery B) connected to a slide wire voltage control D which determines the applied voltage to the anode A and cathode C. In addition the voltage at the surface of the working electrode (in reductions, C) is controlled by comparison with reference electrode E which is connected to a potentiometer F. The total current is measured by the ammeter G.

The major differences between the electrolytic setups diagramed in Figures 11-1 and 11-3 is that the voltage can be varied as the

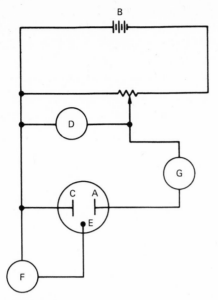

Figure 11-3. Precise electrolytic system.

conditions change in the electrolytic cell of Figure 11-3 and a third, or reference, electrode E is introduced into the cell to monitor the cell conditions. This reference electrode E is attached to a potentiometer F which indicates what changes are needed in the applied voltage in order to keep the voltage constant at the electrode surfaces. Generally, the potentiometer is set to adjust the applied voltage automatically by incorporating the potentiometer and voltage control into a single instrument, called a potentiostat.

Suitable potentiostats are described in several apparatus catalogs, for example, Brinkman (Wenking), Hewlett–Packard, Ryaby Associates (Tacussel).

Variables Important in Organic Electrochemistry

As might be anticipated a large number of variables are involved with organic electrochemistry. Some of these are current, voltage, electrodes, cell construction, solvents, and supporting electrolytes [3].

1. Current and Voltage

As discussed above the voltage at which an electrolysis is run is extremely important, especially if more than one electrochemical process can occur. In order to determine in advance the optimum voltage required for a given electrolysis, it is helpful to run a current-voltage relationship (polarographic) study on the compound to be electrolyzed (see Figure 11-2). A polarograph is relatively simple to do if the necessary equipment is available and can save much time.

Such determinations can be achieved on any of several commercial polarographs (Sargent, Beckman) using a dropping mercury electrode system.

The current will control the length of time that will be required to electrolyze a given quantity of material (presuming that the correct voltage to accomplish electron-transfer is applied). Since an ampere is a coulomb per second, a current of 2 amps will electrolyze 0.5 mole of materials in about 7 hr if the electrolysis involves a one-electron process.

2. Electrodes

Both liquid and solid electrodes [4] are commonly used in organic electrochemistry. A very useful electrode for reduction is a mercury pool. In view of the simplicity involved in preparing a mercury pool electrode, it is not surprising that much of the reductive work on organic compounds which appears in the literature has been carried out at a mercury electrode.

Platinum and carbon rod electrodes are also very often used in organic electrochemistry. Other electrodes which find occasional usage are gold, silver, lead, lead oxide, and carbon paste. Unfortunately, some electrochemical reactions will occur only on specific electrodes. In other cases yields are much higher with some electrodes than with others. In view of the observed specificity it is wise to consult the literature for analogous examples to aid in the choice of electrodes for a given electrochemical conversion [5].

The use of stationary electrodes in a cell often requires vigorous stirring of the solution in order to provide good transport of the material to be electrolyzed to the electrode surface. Magnetic stirring is often advantageous for this purpose. It is also often necessary to stir a mercury electrode in order to keep the surface of the mercury in a noncontaminated condition.

3. Cell Construction

There are many critical features of cell construction which can have a dramatic effect on the failure or success of a given electrolysis.

Cells can be placed into two categories: divided and undivided. The divided cell has a porous barrier separating the solutions surrounding the anode and the cathode. This barrier can consist of any one of numerous porous materials. Porous ceramics, fritted glass, or asbestos are probably the most common materials used to divide the cell [3].

The use of a divided cell is most important when the organic compound being electrolyzed is capable of both oxidation and reduction. The process that takes place can be controlled by restricting the material to the anodic or cathodic compartment. Divided cells are also necessary when the material formed in the anodic process can react chemically with the material generated in the cathodic process. Such a situation often exists when a strong base such as hydroxide is being generated.

In discussing cell construction, the size and positioning of the electrodes is pertinent. The larger the electrodes and the closer the electrodes are together, the smaller will be the applied potential necessary to obtain a reasonable current flow. Since the time required for a given electrochemical process will be proportional to the current flow, the size and positioning of the electrodes will partially determine how long any given electrolysis will take.

It should be noted that the electrodes must be kept far enough apart to allow for a relatively free flow of the solution to be electrolyzed between them.

4. Solvents

In organic electrochemistry the choice of solvent is controlled by many factors. The material to be electrolyzed must be soluble in the solvent. The solvent must be electrochemically stable under the conditions used for the electrolysis. Furthermore, depending on the nature of the specific electrolysis under consideration, the solvent may have to be either protic or aprotic. Perhaps the most important facet of solvent properties is that the solvent must be polar enough to dissolve an electrolyte which will carry the current through the solution. Other considerations in choosing a solvent are boiling point and ease of separation from the electrolysis product.

Since many organic compounds are little soluble in water, pure water is rarely used as a solvent for organic electrochemistry. When the presence of water is desired, pyridine-water or alcohol-water solvent systems are generally used.

Other solvents commonly used are various amines including liquid ammonia, various alcohols including ethylene glycol, acetic acid, dimethyl sulfoxide, acetonitrile, dimethylformamide, hexamethyl phosphoramide, pyridine, diethyl ether, tetrahydrofuran, and dioxane.

5. Supporting Electrolytes

As mentioned above, an ionic material is needed to provide a carrier for current. Since most inorganic salts have low solubility in organic solvents, the ionic materials (supporting electrolytes) available are limited. In extremely polar or aqueous systems, alkali metal salts such as lithium bromide, lithium perchlorate, sodium bromide, sodium perchlorate, potassium bromide, and potassium iodide have been used. However, these salts are not soluble enough in the less polar organic solvents such as tetrahydrofuran. Thus a large organic cation is generally required in order to achieve a satisfactory concentration of electrolytes. Salts commonly used for this purpose are tetraethylammonium perchlorate, tetrabutylammonium perchlorate, tetrabutylammonium hexafluorophosphate, and various tetraalkylammonium p-toluenesulfonates.

Electrochemical Reduction of p-Bromoiodobenzene

Experimental Procedure

Place 400 ml of 90% ethanol and 8.5 g of tetraethylammonium bromide into a 500-ml three-necked round-bottomed flask A equipped (as shown in Figure 11-4) with a reflux condenser B, two adapters C with rubber septa D for electrode parts, and a magnetic stirring bar E (Teflon-coated bars float on mercury). Stir the solution by means of the magnetic stirrer F until the salt is completely dissolved. Approximately 12 ml of mercury G is added to serve as the cathode. p-Bromoiodobenzene (10 g) is added along with 8 g of hydrazine hydrate (which serves as an anodic depolarizer).

In order to balance the electron flow, hydrazine gives up electrons to the anode to generate nitrogen and protons. The protons neutralize the base generated from the reaction of bromobenzene anion with water.

The solution is again stirred until all the organic material is dissolved. A copper wire lead H is inserted through one of the septa D so that the exposed end I is entirely covered by the mercury pool as shown.

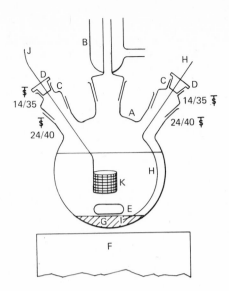

Figure 11-4. Apparatus for electrolysis of *p*-bromoiodobenzene.

The copper wire (18 gauge) is enclosed in Intramedic Polyethylene Tubing (0.045 in. ID, 0.062 in. OD) available from the Clay Adams Co., New York, N.Y., except for that portion connected to the lead wires and that portion extending into the mercury pool. A platinum lead J is inserted in the other septum D so that the gauze anode K of the platinum electrode is suspended approximately 1 in. above the surface of the mercury. Stir the solution vigorously. Connect the negative lead from a dc power supply to the mercury pool electrode H (cathode), and the platinum anode J to the positive pole of the power supply (as in Figure 11-1 or 11-2). Turn the current on and adjust for a current flow of 1 amp. The heat of electrolysis causes the reaction mixture to reflux. With this current flow the electrolysis takes about 5 hr.

The current is turned off, electrodes H and J are removed, and the organic solution is transferred to a 1-liter separatory funnel. Water (300 ml) is added and the solution is extracted with four 100-ml portions of pentane. The combined pentane extracts are back-extracted with two 100-ml portions of saturated sodium chloride and dried over anhydrous magnesium sulfate.

When the solvent used for isolation of reaction products does not contain benzene, drying over magnesium sulfate (or other dessicant) is required rather than mere filtration over a cone of magnesium sulfate (see page 18).

The drying agent is removed by filtration and the solution is concentrated by distillation through a 12-in. helices packed column. The residue is distilled to give 4.78 g (86%) of bromobenzene, bp 54–55°C (20 mm), n_D^{23} 1.5578, as the only product.

Analysis of the crude reaction mixture by vapor pressure chromatography (on a 5 ft column packed with 2% silicone GE XF-1150 on 80/100 Chromasorb G) should show only one impurity which amounts to less than 5% of the bromobenzene. This impurity should not be present in the distilled product.

Electrochemical processes have been used in the synthesis of numerous organic compounds. A few alternative experiments may be suggested. High-voltage electrochemical decarbonylation of carboxylate salts has been used to prepare carbonium ions which can be captured by appropriate nucleophiles [6]. For instance, electrolysis of sodium 1-azabicyclo[2,2,2]octane-2-carboxylate **I** in methanol produces 2-methoxy-1-azabicyclo[2,2,2]octane **II** in 43% yield [7].

An example of a ring closure is provided by the electrolysis of *cis*- and *trans*-1,3-dibromo-1,3-dimethylcyclobutane **III** to produce 1,3-dimethylbicyclobutane **IV** in high yield [8].

REFERENCES

[1] Fry, A. J., M. Mitnick, and Roberta G. Reed, *J. Org. Chem.*, **35**, 1232 (1970).

[2] Rifi, M. R., *J. Org. Chem.*, **36**, 2017 (1971).

[3] For a comprehensive discussion see Weissberger, A., *Technique of Organic Chemistry*, 2nd ed., Interscience Publishers, Inc., New York, 1956.

[4] For a recent discussion of this and other aspects of electrolysis see Adams, R. N., *Electrochemistry at Solid Electrodes*, Marcel Dekker, Inc., New York, 1969.

[5] For a detailed review of electrochemical oxidations in organic chemistry see Weinberg, N. L., and H. R. Weinberg, *Chem. Rev.*, **68**, 449 (1968).

[6] Corey, E. J., and J. Casanova, Jr., *J. Amer. Chem. Soc.*, **85**, 165 (1963); Koehl, Jr., W. J., *J. Amer. Chem. Soc.*, **86**, 4686 (1964); Gassman, P. G., and F. V. Zalar, *J. Amer. Chem. Soc.*, **88**, 2252 (1966).

[7] Gassman, P. G., and B. L. Fox, *J. Org. Chem.*, **32**, 480 (1967).

[8] Rifi, M. R., *J. Amer. Chem. Soc.*, **89**, 4442 (1967).

Twelve

Report Writing

Writing a good report about an experiment is important. The reader of the report should get a clear, concise explanation of why the experiment was undertaken, what the results were, and how the results were obtained. Any conclusions or suggestions for improvement may be placed at the end. In group experiments, the report is the responsibility of the group leader. A suggested form for reports is as follows.

1. Objective
2. Description of experiment
   (a) Apparatus and procedure
   (b) Isolation and purification of products
3. Discussion of results

1. Objective

Your idea of the objective of the experiment should be stated clearly and concisely. In describing the objective of a report to a person, or group, the interest of that person, or group, in the results must be taken into account. Thus, quite different reports might be desirable for the same experiment if presented to persons with different interests. The objectives of the experiments in this book are (in part) to acquaint you with the different laboratory techniques involved. In addition the chemical principles involved in the reactions are also of interest. In all experiments as high a material balance as possible should be sought.

2. Description of Experiment

(a) Apparatus and procedure. Sufficient descriptions of apparatus and procedure should be given so that a reader with a similar background in chemistry would be able to follow the procedure without difficulty.

(b) Isolation and purification of products. The above statement applies here also. In describing techniques such as chromatography and recrystallization, it is insufficient to state that the compound was purified by chromatography and recrystallization. Rather, the amount and kind of adsorbent and the solvents used should be stated. In recrystallization some idea of the amount of pure product obtained on recrystallization of an impure product should be given. It is very annoying to read in the literature that "the yield of product, mp 95–100°C, was 85%. Recrystallization yielded a pure sample, mp 104–105°C." As is often the case, the yield of pure product may be only 40–50%. In other cases, there is little loss on recrystallization. Some estimate of the yield in each step of a multistep synthesis is necessary in order that adequate plans can be made.

Perhaps the best solution to the problem of how much detail to use in reporting an experiment is to put yourself in the position you were in before you performed it. Then give as much detail as you would have found useful when you carried out the experiment.

3. Discussion of Results

Often, in reporting on a single laboratory experiment, there is little in the way of discussion to add. However, any comments concerning the ways in which improvement might be accomplished are desirable. Areas in which suggestions for modifications of the experiment are likely to be found are as follows: solvent, apparatus, order of addition of reactants, concentration of reagents and reactants, methods of estimating how long the reaction mixture should be heated and at what temperature, methods used in separation of the components of the reaction mixture, and purification of the components.

Style for Reports

A copy of *Handbook for Authors of Papers in the Journals of the American Chemical Society*, which can be purchased from the American Chemical Society, 1155 Sixteenth Street, N.W., Washington, D.C., 20036, is extremely useful. Although the report on a laboratory experiment for a course need not be governed by the same requirements as a paper intended for publication, this handbook provides a valuable guide to matters relating to scientific writing. It is helpful to establish a clear and concise style of reporting your work early in your career.

A second valuable source on scientific writing is the "Notice to Authors" printed in certain issues of the *Journal of the American Chemical Society* and the *Journal of Organic Chemistry*. Although these notices are directed to authors of papers to be published in the journals, the suggestions contained therein will help you write concisely.

Finally, after the technical details have been recorded, the English style of the report (and of articles intended for publication) should receive careful attention. The article entitled "Recommended Diet for Padded Writing" by Herman R. Struck is reprinted here. The first draft of your report will be improved by following the suggestions offered. Paring your English style as described in the "Diet" will produce scientific writing that is a source of satisfaction to you and to your readers.

Recommended Diet for Padded Writing[*]

Herman R. Struck

English Department, Michigan State College, East Lansing

From a close examination of the writing in many scientific publications (including, if you do not mind, *The Scientific Monthly*), one would never guess that as a nation we are renowned for efficiency. Sentences bulge like overfed matrons with unnecessary words that obscure a writer's ideas and weaken his emphasis, much as the matronly fat obscures the streamlined glory of the past. For both matrons and sentences, a major solution is diet: for writing, a diet of efficient verbs.

The following sentences from *The Scientific Monthly* illustrate this point:

Whereas [Cannon's] studies have been primarily concerned with the physiological regulations of the internal environment, much of the work of Richter has dealt with the maintenance of the constancy of the internal environment through the operation of behavior regulators.

It is noted by Harrow that pancreatectomy is fatal to the dog, with the death of the animal occurring in one to two weeks and that the length of survival of cats after removal of the pancreas is about five to six days.

Still more unusual is the fact that these surrounding industrial regions give relatively little employment to "Mainliners."

Shorter, clearer, and more forceful versions of these:

. . . Richter has chiefly studied how behavior regulators maintain the constancy of the internal environment.

Harrow notes that pancreatectomy is fatal to dogs in one to two weeks and fatal to cats in about five to six days.

Still more unusual, these surrounding industrial regions employ relatively few "Mainliners."

Since readers may object, with some justification, to criticisms of sentences removed from context, here is a complete—and representative—paragraph, again from *The Scientific Monthly*:

* Reprinted from SCIENCE, April 23, 1954, Vol. 119, No. 3005, pages 522–525.

The decision to stay on a job or leave it, as well as where to work, generally lay with the scientists themselves. Only 18 of the 155 scientists who had remained on their jobs for at least 8 years reported that they had had no other offer or none worth considering during this period. Only 67 of the 574 job exits were due to factors over which the scientists had no control, and 28 of these resulted from the termination of war projects. Furthermore, the scientists were rarely forced to accept a job for lack of another offer; this was the case for only 75 of the 670 job entrances covered by the study. Very likely, the fact that the scientists were able to choose between job offers was at least in part due to their practice of continuing in a position while shopping for a new one: they rarely left a job without having another one lined up.

In this paragraph, as a rewrite shows, more than 10 percent of the words are superfluous:

The scientists themselves could generally decide where to work, and whether to stay on a job or leave it. Only 18 of the 155 scientists who had remained on their jobs for at least 8 years reported that they had had no other offer or none worth considering during this period. Factors over which the scientists had no control accounted for only 67 of the 574 job exits, and termination of war projects caused 28 of these. Furthermore, the scientists rarely had to accept a job for lack of another offer; among 670 job entrances, the study showed only 75 such cases. Very likely, the scientists could choose between job offers partly, at least, because they normally continued in one position while shopping for another: they rarely left a job without having a new one lined up.

Probably most readers will feel the increased crispness and clarity of the revision, particularly in the first and final sentences. The revision uses 137 words against the original's 159.

If any contributor to *The Scientific Monthly* feels impelled at this point to mail a poisoned cake, I should like to remind him that I am not carping about a specific magazine or a specific group of writers. The same excesses appear in other publications as well:

... it *has an opportunity to exercise an unobtrusive influence on* the course of science in the United states . . . [A science review]

. . . it can influence unobtrusively the course of science. . . .

The fact that these teachers overlook *is that the* development of new interests is the job of the teacher. . . . [A book on education]

These teachers overlook the fact that. . . .

Finally, the Midwest was *in the process of swift change* during the nineteenth century. [A history of politics]

. . . the Midwest was changing swiftly. . . .

There is considerable work in the literature *which* supplies supporting, circumstantial evidence for the . . . hypothesis. . . . [A botany journal]

Considerable work in the literature supplies. . . .

Such writing—wherever it appears—hampers the sharp, clear transfer of ideas. And certainly when a writer respects his ideas sufficiently to offer then up to cold print and the tough judgment of his colleagues, he wants to present them as clearly as he can. This he can do more satisfactorily by forcing every verb to do its full duty. The verb, after all, is the spine of a sentence: when the verb falters, the sentence sags, because a less able word must carry the verb idea.

To use verbs efficiently, obviously a writer must first recognize superfluous verbs. This offers some difficulties, but a little practice helps enormously. Moreover, there are some useful guides.

1) Examine all forms of the verb *to be* (*am, is, are, was, were, be, being, been*). If a sentence contains the verb *to be*—and many sentences do—try converting one of the nouns to a verb. Examples (*1*):

... but the experiment *was a complete failure.*

failed completely

... but its persistence *is the result of* two major developments.

stems from

... it *is of concern* also *to* scientists themselves.

it also concerns scientists

In all three types of decisions, *the considerations uppermost in the minds of* most of these scientists *were* the interest of the work, the earnings and opportunities it provided, and the working conditions on the job.

most of these scientists considered primarily the interest of the work (*2*).

Occasionally, in reworking *to be*, the writer will find that converting a noun to a verb does not eliminate *to be* but merely reduces it to a helping verb. In such sentences, certain wordy constructions—often prepositional phrases—needlessly take over some of the verb's function, as in a sentence quoted earlier: "Finally, the Midwest was in the process of swift change during the nineteenth century." Here, *in the process* suggests continuous action; *was* is the main verb. Use of the progressing (*was changing*) eliminates *in the process*, reduces *was* to an auxiliary, and stresses the notion of change.

The constructions *there is* (*there are, there were*, and so forth) and *it is* frequently employ a useless *to be*:

For example, in recent years *there* has *been a tendency for* industry to "decentralize." ...

industry has tended to "decentralize"

Although no figures were available from Daylesford, it is listed because *there is no doubt that* it is the least important stop on the route.

because it is clearly the least important stop

For some men, *it was* the opportunity to develop and grow with a problem *which* was most important.

For some men, the opportunity to develop and grow with a problem was most important.

There is and *it is* require various cures. In the first of the foregoing sentences, for instance, a noun (*tendency*) becomes the main verb (*tended*), replacing *been*; in the second, an adverb (*clearly*) eliminates *there is*; in the third, *it was* and *which* are simply removed.

No one, incidentally, should condemn *to be*—or any other verb or construction that is cudgeled here—automatically. *To be*, to quote a good handbook, "is the most necessary single verb in the language (*3*). But most of us overuse it. Furthermore, a hunt for *to be* synonyms (*exists, consists of*) profits nobody. *Some* word in the existing sentence must carry the real verb idea, and the writer should search for that word; if the verb does not carry the idea, then a noun probably does (*4*).

2) Examine forms of *to have*. Again, look for a key noun. Examples:

These developments *had a profound influence on* Philadelphia's Main Line District.

These developments profoundly influenced

Since these attitudes *have a decided influence on* behavior, information concerning them is valuable to employers, personnel workers, and scientists themselves.

these attitudes strongly influence behavior

... rats *have an ability to* make selections conducive to their well-being.

rats can make selections

3) Look for verbs such as *give, make, do, occur, cause, effect, bring about*. Since a complete list of such verbs would be extremely long, finding them demands sharper eyes than finding *to be* forms. The verbs named are the chronic offenders, however, and a close inspection of nouns will enable a writer to identify the rest.

Though the Catholic Church has neven *given official approbation to* these art forms, they are tolerated. . . .

has never officially approved

A considerable number of scientists also *gave careful consideration to* the prospective working atmosphere in choosing a job.

scientists also considered carefully

... this *brought the end of* tolls.

this ended tolls

A writer should not conclude that these verbs are always unnecessary. In "I gave him the book," *gave* or a synonym is the only verb possible. One must analyze the sentence, especially its nouns, to determine whether or not a particular verb carries the verb idea.

4) Finally, to rephrase a piece of advice that seems only slightly younger than the wheel but almost as useful: convert passive voice constructions that name the doer of the action to the active voice. In the passive voice, you may remember—if your gammar teacher harangued you dutifully—the subject is acted upon. A short sample: "their jobs were threatened by war-created circumstances." Using the doer of the action of subject produces a more brisk wording: "war-created circumstances threatened their jobs." Other examples:

It is rather remarkable that this area has had such a limited development of industry when one considers that *it is surrounded by great industrial regions.*

that great industrial regions surround it

It was during this period that *a cult of the Egyptian Isis was introduced into this area by seagoing natives of Apuglia.*

during this period, seagoing natives of Apuglia introduced into this area a cult of the Egyptian Isis. [This version also removes *it was* and *that.*]

We should mention that *Isis-Horus have/sic/been depicted as black by the Egyptians.*

that the Egyptians have depicted Isis-Horus as black.

A section from a paragraph shows how consistently this construction appears and how it can emasculate ideas (four of the five sentences contain superfluous passives):

Several weeks after these symptoms had developed the animals were placed on the self-selection diet. It *was found* that a marked appetite for fat and olive oil *was shown* by the rats and they ate little or no carbohydrate, which in this experiment was sucrose. An increased appetite *was manifested* by all 7 animals for yeast. On the self-selection diet the diabetic symptoms of all the rats either disappeared or *were* greatly *reduced.* Upon the return to the McCollum diet, diabetic symptoms *were* again *shown* by 4 of the 7 experimental animals.

Without the italicized passives:

Several weeks after these symptoms had developed, the animals were placed on the self-selection diet. The rats then showed a marked appetite for fat and olive oil and ate little or no carbohydrate, which in this experiment was sucrose. All 7 animals manifested an increased appetite for yeast. On the self-selection diet, the diabetic symptoms of all the rats disappeared or greatly decreased. Upon return to the McCollum diet, 4 of the 7 experimental animals again showed diabetic symptoms.

Since *manifested* in the third sentence is a general verb, and since the author uses *ate* in the preceding sentence, I cannot resist offering this version also, though the writer might scream "Distortion!": *All 7 animals ate more yeast.*

Writers who tend to overuse prepositional phrases should be especially wary of the passive, because it frequently requires another prepositional phrase. And an overdose of prepositional phrases can easily send a healthy reader to a sick bed. The last half of a sentence quoted earlier supports this statement reasonably well:

... much *of* the work *of* Richter has dealt *with* the maintenance *of* the constancy *of* the internal environment *through* the operation *of* behavior regulators.

A hurrying reader would probably never thoroughly understand this clause; a careful reader would have to reread it. In fact, a linguistically inclined friend of mine considers this clause a monument to the infinite meanings of *of*. Successive *of* phrases, he declares enthusiastically, force a reader into horrifying mental gyrations. He points out that the five *of* phrases in the sentence are an old-fashioned grammarian's paradise; the first is a partitive genitive (*much of work*); the second, a subjective genitive (*Richter works*) or a possessive genitive (*Richter's work*); the third, an objective genitive (*maintain constancy*); the fourth, a partitive again (he mumbled a little here about a descriptive in reverse); the fifth, a subjective genitive (*regulators operate*) with some possibility of being regarded also as an objective genitive (*operate regulators*). The human mind can stand just so much.

On a less learned plane, I am convinced that, with a few exceptions, a succession of three *of* phrases, or five of any kind, sets up a rocking-chair rhythm so inimical to ordinary prose that it destroys the reader's concentration on meaning. I first became aware of this fact years ago when I was analyzing some 2000 revisions of various writers; since then I have seen no evidence that alters this view and I have seen a good deal that reinforces it. Several interesting *of* sentences, for instance, appear in Fowler and Fowler's *The King's English*:

The signs of the times point to the necessity of the modification of the system of administration.
The first private conference relating to the question of the convocation of representatives of the nation took place yesterday. (5)

The authors revise the first sentence to

It is becoming clear that the administrative system must be modified.

And the second to

The first private conference on national representation took place yesterday. (5)

Science writers' fascination for the passive is deplorable but understandable. For describing experiments, the passive (without the doer) sometimes performs even more efficiently than the active (6). Too, editorial demand for objectivity may force a writer into abandoning "I," which eventually leads him to "the writer," which eventually generates self-consciousness, which finally sends him slinking to the passive. Thus, editorial policy and the passive's efficiency in specific circumstances may develop in the writer a passive-psychosis, a state in which the patient cannot differentiate between a good passive and a bad one. However faulty this diagnosis, something certainly causes the disease, and to cure it a writer might well consider every passive sick until he proves it healthy.

To end this oracle-like piece realistically, I must admit that the preceding facts, even if heeded, will not guarantee entry into prose heaven. On the other hand, they do identify certain major snares and temptations along the way.

REFERENCES AND NOTES

1. All examples, unless a source is given, are from *The Scientific Monthly*. For obvious reasons, I am not citing the titles of articles or the issue, but I will supply this information to anyone who is interested.
2. A minor comment: *the* (before *working*) and *on the job* are unnecessary.
3. Robert J. Geist and Richard Summers, *Current English Composition* (Rinehart, New York, 1951), p. 419.
4. Occasionally an adjective will contain the verb idea: "Clovers and alfalfa *have a greater beneficial effect on* the soil than any of the other legumes" (benefit the soil more). However, the construction seems rare. This example comes from a student paper.
5. H. W. Fowler and F. G. Fowler, *The King's English* (Oxford Univ. Press, London, 3rd ed., 1931), p. 15.
6. This statement does not mean, incidentally, that the passive minus the doer can do no evil; on the contrary, an unscrupulous or careless writer can easily use it to retreat into remoteness with an unsubstantiated "It is generally thought that . . . ," a pronouncement that a comatose reader may accept without the quiver of a brain cell. But to my lay eye, science researchers do not take refuge in the passive unscrupulously.

Appendixes

Common
Solvents

Organic solvents are widely used for recrystallization of solids, for column chromatography, as media in which to carry out reactions, and to control the maximum temperature of a reaction mixture. The following list of solvents is provided to assist the laboratory worker in selecting the proper solvent for any purpose. The boiling points are in degrees centigrade at atmospheric pressure unless otherwise noted.

Water Miscible		*Water Immiscible*	
Acetone	56	Diethyl ether[a]	35
Tetrahydrofuran[a]	64	Pentane[b]	36
Methanol	65	Methylene chloride	40
Ethanol	78	Carbon disulfide	46
Acetonitrile	80	Chloroform	61
2-Propanol	82	Hexane[b]	68
1,2-Dimethoxyethane[a,c]	84	Carbon tetrachloride	76
Triethylamine	90	Ethyl acetate	77
1-Propanol	97	Butyl chloride	78
Nitromethane	101	Benzene	80
Dioxane[a]	102	Cyclohexane	81
Nitroethane	115	Toluene	111
Pyridine	115	Chlorobenzene	132
Acetic acid	118	Ethylbenzene	136
2-Methoxyethanol[d]	125	*m*- and *p*-Xylene	139
2-Ethoxyethanol[e]	135	*o*-Xylene	144
Dimethylformamide[f]	153	*o*-Dichlorobenzene	179
Di-(2-methoxyethyl)ether[a,g]	161		
Dimethylacetamide	165		
Tetramethylurea	177		
Dimethylsulfoxide[h]	189		
Ethylene glycol	198		
N-methylpyrrolidone	200		
γ-Butyrolactone	206		
Hexamethylphosphoramide	232		
Quinoline	237		
Diethyleneglycol	245		
Tetramethylene sulfoxide	114 (14 mm)		
Tetramethylene sulfone[i]	130 (6.5 mm)		

[a] Samples should not be distilled unless a test for peroxides is negative. These solvents react with oxygen to produce peroxides which concentrate in the distilling

flask. If appreciable amounts of peroxide are present in the initial material, violent explosions may occur near the end of a distillation. Test for peroxides by treating a few milliliters of solvent with dilute sulfuric acid and sodium iodide solution. If peroxides are present, free iodine is liberated and a brown-to-violet color is observed. Starch-iodide test paper may also be used after moistening with dilute acid.

[b] Higher-boiling saturated hydrocarbons are available in varying petroleum ether fractions.

[c] Glyme.

[d] Methyl Cellosolve.

[e] Ethyl Cellosolve; higher boiling alkyl cellosolves are also available.

[f] DMF.

[g] Diglyme.

[h] DMSO.

[i] Sulfolane.

A Few Safety Precautions

1. Never use a free flame without checking to see if those working near you are using volatile inflammable solvents.

2. Never leave the laboratory if you are using a free flame in a setup.

3. Never leave flames on when not in use.

4. Whenever a reaction setup requires a period at reflux, some device to ensure smooth boiling must be used. Such devices include the introduction of various solids, such as small porous chips of Teflon, anthracite coal, porous plate or "Boileezers" (Fisher Scientific Co.). If mechanical or magnetic stirring is used, boiling chips are not necessary. *Do not add boiling chips if the liquid has already been heated to the boiling point.*

5. Be sure rubber tubing on condensers is securely attached. Use an appropriately prepared file and glycerine when disconnecting rubber-to-glass connections (see page 27). *More serious cuts result from carelessness in this operation than any other.*

6. Do not use a more rapid stream of water in your condensers than necessary as the tubing may work loose when the water pressure rises in the evening.

7. Never leave a reaction alone in the first stages when it may suddenly "take off."

8. Never leave a reaction mixture boiling unattended when a solid product might separate as the reaction proceeds. Should a solid separate severe bumping might occur.

9. Locate the nearest fire extinguisher so that you will know where it is should you need it. For alkali metal (or hydride) fires, a bucket of sand is preferable to a carbon dioxide extinguisher. *Know where the fire blanket is kept and where the shower is.*

10. Never work in the laboratory alone. Should an accident occur, help should be immediately at hand.

11. Always wear safety goggles when working in the laboratory unless you normally wear glasses. Even if you wear glasses, use goggles whenever performing an unfamiliar reaction.

12. Run reactions in the hood whenever toxic or foul-smelling gases are involved.

13. Always use plastic safety shields whenever running a reaction suspected of explosive tendencies. Use safety gloves when adjusting apparatus in such reactions.

An Advanced Organic Laboratory Course

14. Do not pour inflammable solvents down the sink. Use suitably labeled solvent cans for storing such solvents until safe disposal can be arranged.

15. Always wash thoroughly any part of your body which comes in contact with any unknown chemical.

16. Become familiar with the *Handbook of Laboratory Safety*, published in 1967 by The Chemical Rubber Company, Cleveland, Ohio, 44128. A copy of this book should be available to all.

17. If laboratory operations are left unattended overnight, consult the article entitled "Unattended Laboratory Operations," by D. R. Conlon, *J. Chem. Educ.*, **43**, A589 (July 1966).

Index

Triethylene glycol, solvent in W-K reductions, 138

3,3,5 - Trimethylcyclohexanone, 108, 118

2,4,5-Trimethylphenol, 156

2,4,7-Trinitrofluorenone, complexing agent, 44

U

Ultraviolet light, use of, for following chromatographic separations, 50

for detecting contamination of skin, 50

spectra of benzophenone, acetophenone, acetone, and indene, 176

Upward filtration, 22

Urea, use of instead of tertiary amine, 39

V

Vacuum fractionation, 91

Vacuum sublimation, 65

Vapor phase reactor, 121

Voltage control for electrolysis, 195

W

Wavelength distribution of, 253.7 nm source, 171

"sunlight phosphor", 172

"blacklight phosphor", 172

Wolff-Kishner reduction, 136

Z

Zimmerli gauge, 29

Zincke-Suhl Reaction, 156

NOTES

NOTES

NOTES

NOTES

NOTES

NOTES